Stereochemistry,
Mechanism
and Silicon

McGraw-Hill Series in Advanced Chemistry

BAIR   Introduction to Chemical Instrumentation

BALLHAUSEN   Introduction to Ligand Field Theory

BENSON   The Foundations of Chemical Kinetics

BIEMANN   Mass Spectrometry (Organic Chemical Applications)

DAVIDSON   Statistical Mechanics

DAVYDOV   (*Trans.* Kasha and Oppenheimer) Theory of Molecular Excitons

DEAN   Flame Photometry

DJERASSI   Optical Rotatory Dispersion

ELIEL   Stereochemistry of Carbon Compounds

FITTS   Nonequilibrium Thermodynamics

FRISTROM AND WESTENBERG   Flame Structure

HELFFERICH   Ion Exchange

HILL   Statistical Mechanics

HINE   Physical Organic Chemistry

KIRKWOOD AND OPPENHEIM   Chemical Thermodynamics

KOSOWER   Molecular Biochemistry

LAITINEN   Chemical Analysis

MANDELKERN   Crystallization of Polymers

McDOWELL   Mass Spectrometry

PITZER AND BREWER   (*Revision of* Lewis and Randall) Thermodynamics

POPLE, SCHNEIDER, AND BERNSTEIN   High-resolution Nuclear Magnetic Resonance

PRYOR   Mechanisms of Sulfur Reactions

ROBERTS   Nuclear Magnetic Resonance

ROSSOTTI AND ROSSOTTI   The Determination of Stability Constants

SOMMER   Stereochemistry, Mechanism and Silicon

STREITWIESER   Solvolytic Displacement Reactions

SUNDHEIM   Fused Salts

WIBERG   Laboratory Technique in Organic Chemistry

(+)-α-**Naphthylphenylmethylsilane,**
precursor of more than one hundred
optically active organosilicon compounds.
Photograph by Edward Leos

Leo H. Sommer

Professor of Chemistry
The Pennsylvania State University

McGraw-Hill Book Company

New York
St. Louis
San Francisco
Toronto
London
Sydney

Stereochemistry, Mechanism and Silicon

An Introduction to the Dynamic Stereochemistry and Reaction Mechanisms of Silicon Centers

Stereochemistry, Mechanism and Silicon:

An Introduction to the Dynamic Stereochemistry and
Reaction Mechanisms of Silicon Centers

Library of Congress Catalog Card Number 64-23281

59640

1296411

To my good friends at Dow Corning Corporation—
in warm appreciation of many years of constant
help, generous support, and shared enthusiasm for
organosilicon research.

Preface

In comparison to the carbon centers of organic compounds, reaction rates of silicon centers in organosilicon compounds are frequently too fast to measure by conventional techniques, and this fact greatly complicates the effort to acquire fundamental information concerning reaction mechanisms. (The same is generally true of phosphorus, germanium, and tin compounds.) In this situation, knowledge of the dynamic (reaction) stereochemistry of such compounds can be of great help in elucidating reaction mechanisms, and this book deals with the development of the new field of organosilicon stereochemistry and its mechanism implications.

Before 1958 the stereochemistry of nucleophilic substitution at silicon centers was completely unknown. However, at the time of this writing, more than a hundred reactions of optically active organosilicon compounds have been studied and have had their stereochemistry elucidated; the absolute configurations of many optically active organosilicon compounds have been determined; and the stereochemical data reveal that the silicon atom is a highly sophisticated reaction center whose mechanism paths are multiple.

The scientific and technological importance of silicon compounds justifies the conclusion that the subject of this book will be of interest to many chemists in many countries. I can only hope that my treatment of it has been adequate.

I wish to acknowledge my great debt to all my students, and in particular to those who labored so diligently in the effort to unravel the mysteries of organosilicon stereochemistry, namely: Cecil L. Frye (who first synthesized R_3Si^*H), O. Francis Bennett, Martin C. Musolf, Forrest O. Stark, Norman C. Lloyd, G. Anthony Parker, Paul G. Rodewald, Keith W. Michael, and William D. Korte.

For their dedicated efforts, I would like to thank all my teachers, including Frank C. Whitmore, whose memory is still fresh in the hearts of many organic chemists, and my most important teacher, my father, Harry Sommer.

I wish to thank Professors Robert A. Benkeser and Dietmar Seyferth for their criticism of the original manuscript. Their valuable suggestions have been most helpful.

The patience and understanding of my wife, Sara, have made it possible for me to write this book, and the diligent efforts of my secretary, Mrs. N. Fischer, have produced the final draft of the manuscript in record time.

Finally, I am grateful to the John Simon Guggenheim Memorial Foundation for the opportunity to write a sizable part of this book while being away from the press of my usual duties and enjoying the hospitality of friends at Harvard University.

Leo H. Sommer

University Park, Pennsylvania
January 1964

Contents

Preface   XI

one   Fundamental considerations   1

1-1 Introduction   *2*

1-2 sp^3 σ-Bonding and tetrahedral geometry   *2*

1-3 π-Bonding   *3*

1-4 The $3d$ orbitals   *4*

1-5 σ-Bonding and the $3d$ orbitals   *5*

1-6 Bond energy, bond refraction, and bond polarity   *24*

1-7 Siliconium ions   *28*

1-8 Organosilyl free radicals and silanions   *37*

two   **Optically active compounds   39**

2-1   Synthesis of optically active α-NpPhMeSiX compounds (R$_3$Si*X)   *40*

2-2   Assignment of relative configuration   *43*

2-3   Special need for stereochemical studies of compounds of second-row elements   *43*

three   **Stereochemistry and mechanisms of silicon-oxygen bonds   47**

3-1   Introduction   *48*

3-2   Syntheses   *48*

3-3   Grignard reduction of R$_3$Si*OMe: a four-center retention mechanism   *49*

3-4   Retention reactions of R$_3$Si*OR' and R$_3$Si*OSi*R$_3$ *51*

3-5   Mechanisms of R$_3$Si*OR' compounds: discussion of S$_N$i-Si and S$_N$2-Si mechanisms   *56*

3-6   Inversion reactions of R$_3$Si*OCOR'   *66*

3-7   An inversion reaction for R$_3$Si*OTs   *70*

3-8   Mechanism S$_N$2-Si for R$_3$Si*OCOR'   *72*

3-9   Summary of stereochemistry and mechanisms for R$_3$Si*—O— compounds   *73*

four   **Stereochemistry and mechanisms of silicon-halogen bonds   75**

4-1   Introduction   *76*

4-2   Inversion: a common stereochemical path for R$_3$Si*Cl and R$_3$Si*Br   *78*

4-3   Solvent-induced racemization of R$_3$Si*Cl: evidence for an ionization mechanism   *84*

4-4   Inversion and retention reactions of R$_3$Si*F   *87*

4-5   Racemization of R$_3$Si*F without displacement of fluoride ion: expanded-octet (EO) return   *88*

4-6   Mechanisms of R$_3$Si*Hal compounds: discussion of S$_N$2-Si, S$_N$1-Si, S$_N$2*-Si, and S$_N$i-Si mechanisms   *91*

4-7 Summary of stereochemistry and mechanisms for R$_3$Si*Hal compounds *93*

five **Halide-halide exchange at asymmetric silicon: S$_N$2-Si and S$_N$1-Si mechanisms 95**

5-1 Introduction *96*
5-2 Halide-halide exchange by mechanism S$_N$2-Si *96*
5-3 Racemization of R$_3$Si*Cl by cyclohexylammonium salts *97*
5-4 Chloride-chloride exchange at asymmetric silicon *98*

six **Stereochemistry and mechanisms of R$_3$Si*H 101**

6-1 Introduction *102*
6-2 Deuterium-hydrogen exchange with retention of configuration *102*
6-3 Retention reactions of R$_3$Si*H with oxygen-containing bases *104*
6-4 Retention reactions of R$_3$Si*H with chlorine and bromine *107*
6-5 A retention reaction of R$_3$Si*H with perbenzoic acid *110*
6-6 Summary of stereochemistry and mechanisms of R$_3$Si*H *110*

seven **Relative and absolute configurations of α-naphthylphenylmethylsilanes 113**

7-1 Introduction *114*
7-2 Chemical correlations of configuration *114*
7-3 X-ray application of the Fredga method *116*
7-4 Optical rotatory dispersion *121*
7-5 Absolute configurations *123*

eight **Structure and reactivity 125**

8-1 Introduction *126*
8-2 Polar and steric effects of substituents *127*

8-3   Effects of the leaving group and the reagent   *146*

8-4   Effects of the solvent   *150*

nine   **Bridgehead silicon   153**

9-1   Introduction   *154*

9-2   Bridgehead silicon chlorides   *154*

9-3   Bridgehead silicon hydrides   *156*

9-4   Chloride-chloride exchange at bridgehead silicon   *158*

ten   **Recent advances   161**

10-1   New optically active systems   *162*

10-2   Coupling reactions with organometallic reagents: significance for mechanism   *166*

eleven   **A general survey of the stereochemistry and mechanisms of silicon centers   173**

11-1   Introduction   *174*

11-2   Reaction profiles for S_N2-Si and S_Ni-Si mechanisms   *174*

11-3   The S_N2-Si mechanism   *175*

11-4   The S_Ni-Si mechanism   *176*

11-5   The S_N1-Si ionization mechanism   *178*

11-6   The S_N2*-Si mechanism   *179*

11-7   The S_N2**-Si mechanism   *180*

11-8   The principle of "least motion" of nonreacting groups   *182*

11-9   The S_N2-Si stereochemistry rule and participation of the $3d_{z^2}$ orbital   *184*

Index of reactions   187

Stereochemistry,
Mechanism
and Silicon

chapter
one **Fundamental considerations**

1-1 Introduction

The general problem of formulating the mechanisms of chemical reactions is a complex one. A major difficulty is posed by the nature of one of the three types of structures that are of interest in the reaction process. Thus, in general, we have:

Reactant state $\longrightarrow$ Transition state(s)

Product state

and only the first and third are stable chemical species whose properties are subject to direct experimental study. Conclusions with regard to the second are one step further removed from direct observation and are therefore based on evidence that is much more circumstantial than that usually adduced for the other two. In these circumstances, a reaction mechanism is properly regarded as the best hypothesis that can be put forward on the basis of the data available at the time that it is formulated—in short, a reaction mechanism is not necessarily invariant with time, and in this important respect is different from the experimental facts upon which it is based.

It is reasonable to begin the discussion of polar mechanisms of organosilicon reactions with a consideration of pertinent structure and energy parameters for stable compounds of silicon. It is evident that these are germane to the problem of postulating transition states.

1-2 sp^3 σ-Bonding and tetrahedral geometry

If we examine the structural data available for a large number of acyclic compounds of silicon, we conclude that the vast majority of these substances contain tetravalent, tetrahedral silicon. (Noteworthy exceptions are discussed in Sec. 1-5.)

Representative inorganic compounds of silicon in which directly attached atoms make a tetrahedral angle with the central silicon atom are SiH_4, SiF_4, $SiCl_4$, $SiBr_4$, SiI_4, $SiHCl_3$, SiH_2Cl_2, SiH_3Cl, $(SiCl_3)_2O$, $Cl_3SiSiCl_3$, and α-quartz.[1]

Representative organosilicon compounds which also have this geometry are[1] $(CH_3)_4Si$, $(CH_3)_3SiCl$, $(CH_3)_2SiCl_2$, CH_3SiCl_3, $(CH_3)_2SiBr_2$, $[(CH_3)_3Si]_2O$, and $(CH_3)_3SiSi(CH_3)_3$.

These data, taken along with a consideration of the relative energies of the $3s$, $3p$, and $3d$ orbitals, lead to the conclusion that silicon, like carbon, prefers to use sp^3 σ-bonding in most of its compounds. There exists, therefore, a wide-ranging structural similarity between the compounds of silicon and of carbon, at least with regard to bonding type in σ-bonding and molecular geometry. However, with regard to π-bonding, we shall briefly note striking differences between the compounds of these two elements in the next section.

1-3 π-Bonding

The great importance of p_π-p_π multiple bonding in organic chemistry is not paralleled by a similar importance of this type of bonding for silicon. No well-authenticated case of p_π-p_π multiple bonding for silicon is known.[2]

A very different type of multiple bonding is apparently possible for silicon, and involves silicon as an electron acceptor in dative d_π-p_π bonding. Linkages postulated to involve such bonding include silicon-oxygen, silicon-halogen, silicon-nitrogen, and silicon-aryl. Various lines of evidence for the reality of this type of bonding have been reviewed recently.[3] They include: bond shortening below the sum of the covalent radii, after correction for electronegativity differences; the planar structure of $(SiH_3)_3N$; the large Si—O—Si bond angles in many compounds, ca. 130 to 150°; dipole moment data; hydrogen bonding studies of silicon-oxygen bonds as proton acceptors.[4]

---

[1] For specific references see "Interatomic Distances," Special Publication No. 11 of The Chemical Society, Burlington House, London, 1958.

[2] The fundamental reasons for this do not seem to be clearly defined as yet.

[3] C. Eaborn, "Organosilicon Compounds," Butterworth & Co. (Publishers), Ltd., London, 1960, pp. 94–103.

[4] R. West, L. S. Watley, and K. J. Lake, *J. Am. Chem. Soc.,* **83,** 761 (1961).

Unlike p_π-p_π bonding, this type of multiple bonding does not affect freedom of rotation about the σ-bond connecting the two atoms (presumably because of the diffuse nature of $3d$ versus $3p$ orbitals). Nor does it affect the σ-bond geometry about the silicon atom; the F—Si—F angle is tetrahedral in SiF_4, and various cases, including those in Sec. 1-2, support this conclusion. Thus, the significance of d_π-p_π bonding for primary effects on the geometry of organosilicon transition states is difficult to discern.

1-4   The $3d$ orbitals

The $3d$ orbitals—in contrast to p orbitals—do not all have the same shape and relative orientation in space.[5] (See Fig. 1-1.) Following the convention adopted in ligand-field theory, they may be divided into two groups. The d_γ orbitals, d_{z^2} and

[5] The first part of this discussion of $3d$ orbitals parallels the excellent summary by R. J. Gillespie and R. S. Nyholm, in "Progress in Stereochemistry," vol. 2, Butterworths Scientific Publications, London, 1958, chap. 8, pp. 276–278.

Fig. 1-1   The shapes and relative orientation of $3d$ orbitals.

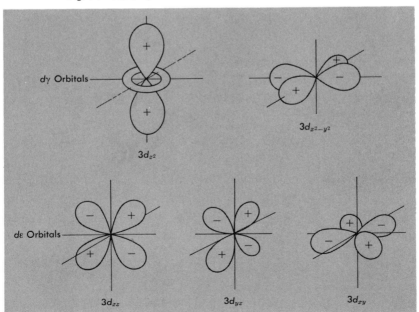

$d_{x^2-y^2}$, are directed along the same x, y, and z axes as the p orbitals. The d_ε orbitals, d_{xy}, d_{xz}, and d_{yz}, have their maxima in directions at 45° to the x, y, and z axes and have nodes in the directions of these axes. For σ-bonding of nontransitional elements (including silicon), the d_γ orbitals are most suitable for use in addition to one s and three p orbitals, sp^3d and sp^3d^2 hybridization, whereas the d_ε orbitals are the most suitable for d_π-p_π bonding.

1-5   σ-Bonding and the $3d$ orbitals

From the vantage point of current knowledge concerning the reaction mechanisms of carbon, it is clear that the relatively early recognition of the existence of stable chemical species in which the valence of carbon is less than 4 provided clues which were very significant. Thus, time has confirmed the important role of carbonium ions and organic free radicals as reaction intermediates in organic chemistry. It is therefore of interest to inquire concerning the existence of *stable* chemical species in which the valence of silicon also deviates from 4 as far as σ-bonding is concerned. In this section, valence in excess of 4 is considered for silicon. Free radicals and siliconium ions are discussed later.

The fluorosilicate anion and related phosphorus compounds

This example of expanded-octet silicon has long been known, and x-ray diffraction studies on its salts [e.g., $CaSiF_6$, K_2SiF_6, $(NH_4)_2SiF_6$] have revealed its octahedral geometry and yielded an Si—F bond distance reported as 1.71 Å. (ref. 1). These studies, made before 1945, have a probable uncertainty of ±0.02 Å., and hence the reported value cannot be differentiated from the Si—F bond length after Schomaker-Stevenson correction for ionic character, 1.687 Å. Little or no π-bonding is indicated for this structure.

The corresponding chloro-, bromo-, and iodosilicates are unknown, and it is generally assumed that the combination of high electronegativity and small size of F substituents makes the $SiF_6^=$ structure possible. The importance of the electronega-

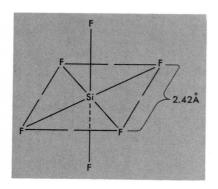

Fig. 1-2 The SiF$_6^=$ ion.

tivity factor is clearly indicated by the existence of the octa-hedral hexachlorophosphate anion, PCl$_6^-$, in combination with PCl$_4^+$ in the crystalline form of PCl$_5$, when it is recalled that the covalent radius of phosphorus is 1.10 Å. compared to 1.18 Å. for silicon.[1] In PCl$_6^-$ the average P—Cl bond length is 2.07 Å., relative to an average Si—Cl length for tetravalent silicon chlorides of 2.03 Å., but it seems certain that an SiCl$_6^=$ species, if it existed, would have an Si—Cl bond length in excess of 2.07 Å. Thus, the nonbonded atom repulsions in the hypothetical hexa-chlorosilicate anion should not be prohibitive from the standpoint of interatomic distances. It is interesting to note that for PCl$_6^-$ the cis Cl—Cl distances are 2.92 Å. as compared to 2.887 Å. for CCl$_4$. (See Fig. 1-3.)

The nonexistence of a stable SiCl$_6^=$ species demonstrates that other factors are also important, including electronegativity of attached groups as well as the difference in formal charge of PCl$_6^-$ and SiCl$_6^=$. The PF$_6^-$ anion is known in the solid compound KPF$_6$.

Stable pentacovalent-silicon anions, e.g., SiF$_5^-$, are un-known,* but neutral compounds of pentavalent phosphorus have long been recognized as stable molecular species. Studies of the molecular structures of PF$_5$, PCl$_5$, and PF$_3$Cl$_2$ in the vapor state clearly indicate a *trigonal bipyramid* geometry for all three substances.[6] For PCl$_5$, the apical bonds (2.19 ± 0.02 Å.) are significantly longer than the equatorial bonds (2.04 ± 0.06 Å.).[1]

---

* *Added in proof:* C. L. Frye [*J. Am. Chem. Soc.,* **86,** 3171 (1964)] has recently furnished elegant proof for the existence of pentacovalent-silicon anions in the amine salts of bis(o-arylenedioxy)organosiliconic acids.

[6] L. O. Brockway and J. Y. Beach, *J. Am. Chem. Soc.,* **60,** 1836 (1938).

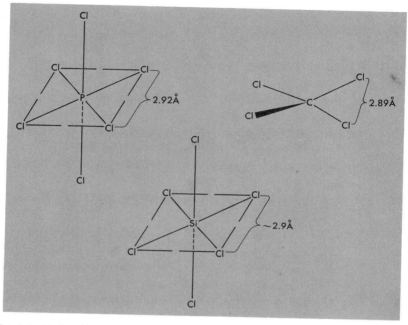

Fig. 1-3 Nonbonded chlorine-chlorine distances in PCl_6^-, CCl_4, and the hypothetical $SiCl_6^=$ ion.

In PCl_5, the Cl—Cl distances are 2.99 Å. for apical-equatorial and 3.53 Å. for equatorial-equatorial. These distances and the Cl—Cl distances in the hypothetical $SiCl_5^-$ ion would be approximately the same. In both cases, the apical-equatorial Cl—Cl distance is approximately the same as the Cl—Cl distance in CCl_4, ~ 2.9 Å.

Pure liquid PCl_5 is unionized and also has a trigonal bipyramidal structure, as indicated by its Raman spectrum.[7] However, transference experiments indicate that the ions PCl_4^+ and PCl_6^- are formed when PCl_5 is dissolved in nitrobenzene.[8] In solvents such as carbon tetrachloride and carbon disulfide, the extent of ionization is small, as indicated by conductivity measurements and dielectric constant studies.[9]

The above structural data for $SiF_6^=$ and related expanded-

[7] H. Moreau, M. Magat, and G. Wetroff, *Compt. rend.,* **205,** 276, 545 (1937).

[8] D. S. Payne, *J. Chem. Soc.,* 1052 (1953).

[9] P. Trunel, *Compt. rend.,* **202,** 37 (1936); J. H. Simons and G. Jessop, *J. Am. Chem. Soc.,* 1263 (1931).

octet phosphorus compounds are of interest in connection with subsequent discussion of organosilicon transition states. *They indicate, at once, that reaction intermediates containing penta-covalent or hexacovalent silicon cannot be ruled out on the basis of prohibitive nonbonded atom repulsions.* However, they do not, of course, tell us that such reaction intermediates are used by organosilicon reaction mechanisms—the situation is much too complex for any such simple and unequivocal decision—but rather that it is possible that some reactions pursue such a path under conditions more favorable to it than to other reaction mechanisms.

For the nontransitional elements, outer d orbitals used in expanded-octet bonding are of higher energy than s or p orbitals. Therefore, d orbitals are only used in addition to one s and three p orbitals. A σ-bonding covalence of 5 requires the use of one d orbital. If the one used for hybridization is the d_{z^2} orbital, then the predicted molecular geometry is a trigonal bipyramid, in accord with the known structures of PF_5, PCl_5 (vapor), and PF_3Cl_2. From consideration of the complete wave function, Linnett and Mellish have concluded that the most probable arrangement of five electrons with the same spin in the configuration $(s)(p)^3 (d_{z^2})$ is at the corners of a trigonal bipyramid.[10] However, the most probable arrangement for the configuration $(s)(p)^3 (d_{x^2-y^2})$ is a tetragonal pyramid in which the four basal electrons are not coplanar with the central nucleus but make an angle of ca. 105° with it and the apical electron.[10] Trigonal bipyramid and tetragonal pyramid arrangements for silicon are shown in Fig. 1-4.

A σ-bonding covalence of 6 requires the use of two d orbitals, and these will be the d_γ orbitals. Linnett and Mellish have shown that the most probable arrangement of six electrons with the same spin in the configuration $(s)(p)^3 (d_{z^2}) (d_{x^2-y^2})$ is at the corners of an octahedron. Thus, in any molecule in which there are six pairs of electrons in the valence shell of a nontransitional element, the bonds to the central atom will have an octahedral arrangement.[10]

To a first approximation, the bonding in $SiF_6^=$, PF_6^-, and PCl_6^- may be described as sp^3d^2 for all six bonds, and for

[10] J. W. Linnett and C. E. Mellish, *Trans. Faraday Soc.,* **50,** 655 (1954).

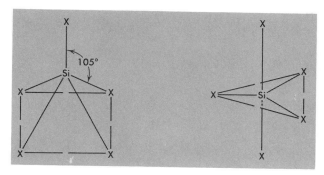

Fig. 1-4 Tetragonal pyramid and trigonal bipyramid geometry for pentacovalent silicon.

PCl_5 (vapor), PF_5, and PF_3Cl_2, the bonding may be designated sp^3d for all five bonds. In fact, the situation is probably not so simple.

An optically active hexacovalent-silicon cation

In 1903 W. Dilthey[11] postulated that the product obtained from treatment of silicon tetrachloride with acetylacetone, $A_3SiCl \cdot HCl$, contains hexacoordinate silicon (A = the acetylacetonate group, $C_5H_7O_2$—). In 1958, a brilliant piece of experimental work by S. Kirschner et al.[12] confirmed Dilthey's hypothesis.

Treatment of $A_3SiCl \cdot HCl$ with the disodium salt of D(—)-dibenzoyltartaric acid gave

$$
\begin{array}{l}
CO_2Na \\
| \\
CHOCOC_6H_5 \\
| \\
CHOCOC_6H_5 \\
| \\
CO_2Na
\end{array}
\;+\;
\begin{array}{l}
L\text{-}[A_3Si]Cl \cdot HCl \\
D\text{-}[A_3Si]Cl \cdot HCl
\end{array}
\;\longrightarrow
$$

$$
\begin{array}{l}
CO_2{}^-[L\text{-}A_3Si]^+ \\
| \\
CHOCOC_6H_5 \\
| \\
CHOCOC_6H_5 \\
| \\
CO_2H
\end{array}
\;+\; D\text{-}[A_3Si]Cl \cdot HCl \;+\; 2NaCl
$$

$$I$$

[11] W. Dilthey, *Ber.*, **36,** 923 (1903); *Ann.*, **344,** 300 (1906).
[12] S. K. Dhar, V. Doron, and S. Kirschner, *J. Am. Chem. Soc.*, **80,** 753 (1958).

and substance I, which crystallized out preferentially (D- and L-
are purely arbitrary for the silicon compounds), was then treated
with an anion-exchange resin in chloride form,

$$\text{I} + \text{resin—Cl} \longrightarrow \text{L-}(-)[A_3Si]Cl \cdot HCl \text{ (II)}$$

which gave optically active II for which a 0.0311% solution had
$\alpha_{obs.}$ $-0.300 \pm 0.003°$, corresponding to $[\alpha]_D$ $-965°$.   The
dextrorotatory isomer, $[\alpha]_D + 679°$, was also obtained.   These
facts clearly show that the acetylacetonate groups are bonded to
silicon in such a way as to provide the asymmetry requisite for
optical activity.   In fact, they lead directly and unequivocally to
the hypothesis of an octahedral geometry for a hexacovalent-
silicon cation bearing unit positive charge.   The rest of the
molecule is probably the hydrogen dichloride anion HCl_2^-, which
is known to form stable salts with large cations.[13]

It is interesting and important to note that the optical
rotation of II decreased and decayed to zero in 6 hours.   The
half-life of the racemization was only about one hour,[12] thus indicating a considerable degree of instability for the octahedral
bonding, presumably sp^3d^2, in II.   It is also pertinent to note
here that analogous hexacovalent-silicon cations in which the six
oxygen functions are part of simple alkoxy groups, RO—, are
unknown.   Thus, one major factor contributing to the existence
of II may be the high resonance energy of the acetylacetonate
groups.

Structural limitations on formation of expanded-octet silicon acetylacetonates

In a significant investigation, R. West[14] has studied the infrared
spectra of a variety of substances derived from reaction of acetylacetone with silicon chlorides.   Pertinent data are given in
Table 1-1.   The discussion which follows largely parallels that
given by West.[14]   It is included here because it is important
to assess the evidence for the significant conclusions which were
drawn.

[13] H. F. Herbrandson, R. T. Dickerson, and J. Weinstein, *J. Am. Chem. Soc.,* **76,**
4046 (1954).

[14] R. West, *J. Am. Chem. Soc.,* **80,** 3246 (1958).

Table 1-1
Infrared absorption bands for acetylacetonates[a]

Compound	1500–1800 cm.$^{-1}$	950–1050 cm.$^{-1}$
$A_3Si^+HCl_2^-$	1555	1023
$MeSiA_2Cl$	1550	1033
$C_6H_5SiA_2Cl$	1553	1047
Me_2SiA_2	1595 (1620) 1669	1030
Me_3SiA	1592 (1620) 1678	1025 (982)
$(Et)_3SiA$	1592 (1620) 1681	1010 (1033)
$Me_3Si(C_6H_9O_2)^b$	1587 (1610) 1672	994
$C_2H_5A^c$	1580 (1626) 1671	

[a] Weak bands or shoulders are given in parentheses.
[b] 2-Trimethylsiloxy-3-methyl-2-pentene-4-one.
[c] 2-Ethoxy-2-pentene-4-one.

From the previous discussion it is clear that the strong 1555-cm.$^{-1}$ band for $A_3Si^+HCl_2^-$ must be assigned to C—O bonds which, for each individual acetylacetonate group, are both bonded to silicon. The conjugated (but nonchelated) carbonyl group in the enol ether of acetylacetone, 2-ethoxy-2-pentene-4-one, has a strong carbonyl band at 1671 cm.$^{-1}$. The latter band, significantly, is present in the infrared spectra for the last five compounds but absent for the first three in Table 1-1. On the other hand, the strong band at 1555 cm.$^{-1}$ for $A_3Si^+HCl_2^-$ is apparently present in the first three and absent in the last five infrared spectra—this type of absorption is found in metal chelates of acetylacetone, all of which have one or two strong bands in the 1500- to 1600-cm.$^{-1}$ region.[15] For the last five compounds in Table 1-1 the presence of strong bands at 1580 to 1595 cm.$^{-1}$ might be attributed to a shift of the 1555-cm.$^{-1}$ band in $A_3Si^+HCl_2^-$, but this does not accord with the fact of a necessarily unchelated structure for C_2H_5A. These bands (1580 to 1595 cm.$^{-1}$) are assigned by West to a C=C vibration, enhanced in intensity and shifted to lower frequency by a conjugated carbonyl substituent. This assignment is in accord with other infrared data.[16]

[15] J. Lecomte, *Disc. Faraday Soc.*, **9**, 125 (1950); R. West and R. Riley, *J. Inorg. Nucl. Chem.*, **5**, 295 (1958).

[16] R. S. Rasmussen, D. D. Tunnicliff, and R. R. Brattain, *J. Am. Chem. Soc.*, **71**, 1068 (1949).

Compelling evidence is provided by West for O-silylated rather than C-silylated structures for the silicon-acetylacetonates in Table 1-1, and the bands in the 994- to 1047-cm.$^{-1}$ range are attributed to Si—O vibrations. This assignment is in accord with other infrared studies of Si—O compounds.

On balance, the infrared data are fairly convincing on the point of expanded-octet σ-bonding for silicon in $A_3Si^+HCl_2^-$, $MeSiA_2Cl$, and $C_6H_5SiA_2Cl$, and also indicate the absence of such bonding in Me_2SiA_2, Me_3SiA, and Et_3SiA. For $A_3Si^+HCl_2^-$, independent evidence indicates the presence of hexacovalent silicon. For $MeSiA_2Cl$ and $C_6H_5SiA_2Cl$, ionic bonds to Cl would make the silicon pentacovalent, whereas covalent Si—Cl bonds would require hexacovalency. The nature of the Si—Cl bonds in these compounds is not known.

Failure of silicon in Me_3SiY to give expanded-octet σ-bonding

In 1954 an extensive series of formally tetravalent-silicon compounds containing the Me_3Si group was prepared and studied by infrared spectroscopy for the purpose of ascertaining whether expanded-octet σ-bonding involving that group could be detected in cases which appeared favorable to operation of such bonding.[17] The basic idea and technique were the same as those employed later by West[14] in the work just discussed. However, the compounds studied were limited to silicon in the Me_3Si group except for one case. Also, with one exception, the silicon compounds contained carbonyl groups in favorable intramolecular position for coordination with silicon, and the method used was to determine their infrared spectra and to compare the wavelengths of their carbonyl bands with those for three classes of analogous compounds: (1) structures in which hydrogen bonding to the carbonyl group is known or strongly suspected to occur; (2) formally trivalent-boron structures in which the boron should act as an electron acceptor toward the carbonyl; (3) formally Cu^{++} compounds in which the copper is known to chelate with the carbonyl. Five series of such structures were investigated and are designated below in unchelated form.

[17] L. H. Sommer and W. H. Knoth, unpublished work; cf. W. H. Knoth, Ph.D. Thesis, The Pennsylvania State University, January, 1954.

Series I

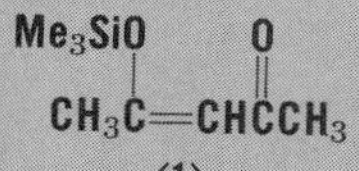

Me₃SiO group: $CH_3C{=}CHCCH_3$ (1)

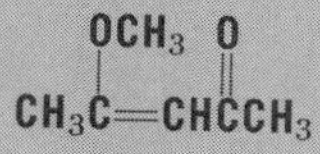

OCH_3 $CH_3C{=}CHCCH_3$ (2)

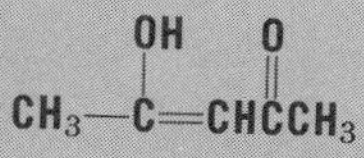

OH $CH_3C{=}CHCCH_3$ (3)

OBF_2 $CH_3C{=}CHCCH_3$ 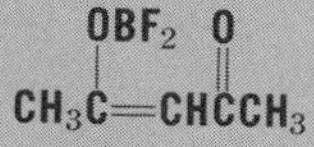 (4)

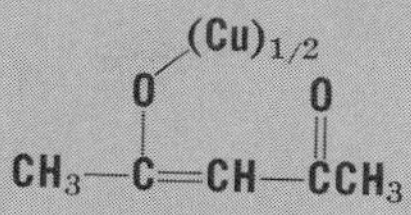

$(Cu)_{1/2}$ $CH_3{-}C{=}CH{-}CCH_3$ (5)

Series II

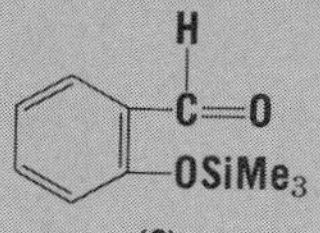

(6) OSiMe₃ benzaldehyde derivative

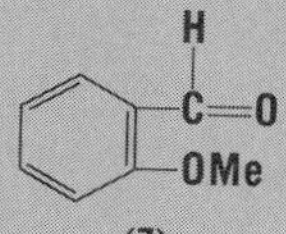

(7) OMe

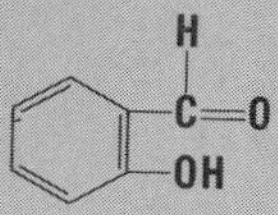

(8) OH

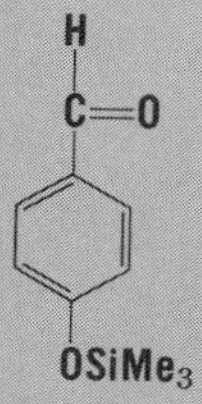

(9) OSiMe₃

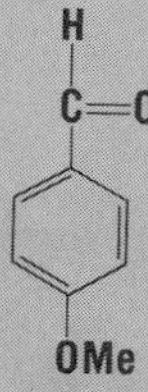

(10) OMe

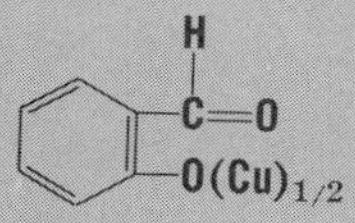

(11) O(Cu)₁/₂

Series III

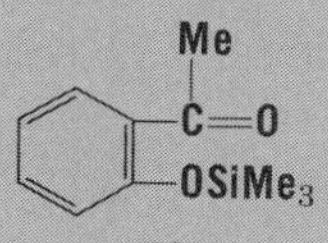

(12) Me, C=O, OSiMe₃

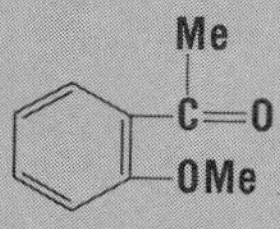

(13) Me, C=O, OMe

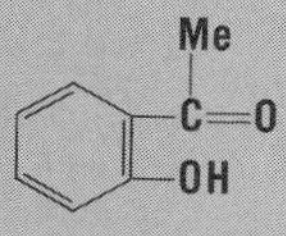

(14) Me, C=O, OH

Series IV

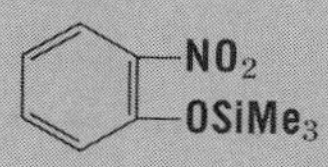

(15) NO₂, OSiMe₃

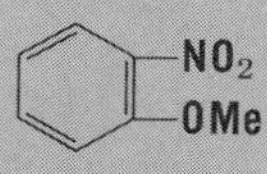

(16) NO₂, OMe

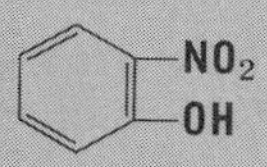

(17) NO₂, OH

Series V

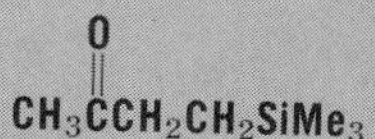

$CH_3CCH_2CH_2SiMe_3$ (18)

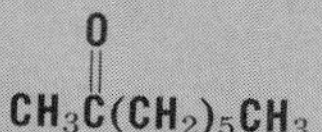

$CH_3C(CH_2)_5CH_3$ (19)

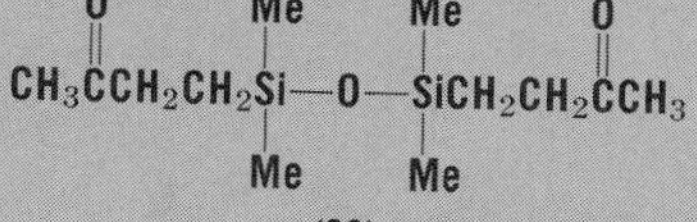

$CH_3CCH_2CH_2Si{-}O{-}SiCH_2CH_2CCH_3$ (20)

Table 1-2
Carbonyl absorption bands for Me_3SiY and related compounds

Compound	Wavelength, μ	Compound	Wavelength, μ
I-1	5.94, 6.04	II-10	5.88
I-2[a]	5.94	II-11	6.21
I-2[b]	6.04	III-12	5.94
I-3	6.22	III-13	5.97
I-4	6.45	III-14	6.08
I-5	6.36	IV-15	7.39[c]
II-6	5.92	IV-16	7.38[c]
II-7	5.92	IV-17	7.52[c]
II-8	6.01	V-18	5.82
II-9	5.88	V-19	5.82
		V-20	5.82

[a] Mostly trans.
[b] Mostly cis.
[c] Bands for —NO_2 group.

The data in Table 1-2 for compounds in series I confirm the conclusions of West with regard to nonchelation of the silicon in Me_3SiA. In our work with I-1, two carbonyl bands were found which correspond exactly to those for the cis and trans isomers of I-2. The silicon compound I-1 is largely trans. The large shifts toward longer wavelength and lower frequency for I-4 (1500 cm.$^{-1}$) and I-5 (1570 cm.$^{-1}$), which certainly must result from chelation with the carbonyl group, are convincing evidence for West's proposal of expanded-octet silicon in $A_3Si^+HCl_2^-$, CH_3SiA_2Cl, and $C_6H_5SiA_2Cl$, but not in Me_2SiA_2 and Me_3SiA.

In series II, the data clearly indicate that despite a favorable geometry which must hold the silicon and carbonyl oxygen in relatively close proximity, there is no effective chelation with Me_3Si. The latter appears to be no more effective than CH_3, whereas hydrogen bonding or chelation with Cu^{++} gives significant shifts toward longer wavelength.

In series III, there is again evidence that Me_3Si and CH_3 are equally ineffective, whereas hydrogen bonding is significant. In series IV exactly the same situation obtains again.

In series V, the Me_2RSiO group in a disiloxane is shown to be ineffective for chelation with carbonyl in acyclic systems, and

V-18 again shows no discernible expanded-octet bonding for Me_3Si.

Evidence for the reluctance of Me_3Si to give expanded-octet bonding may also be adduced from other lines of investigation. The infrared data show no chelation or expanded-octet coordination for tetravalent silicon in Me_3SiO- or in Me_3SiR, when the medium is carbon tetrachloride—a solvent of relatively low ionizing power. In good ionizing solvents such as water, the same situation apparently obtains, as indicated by the acid and base strengths of the following substances:

$$Me_3Si \overset{\displaystyle CH_2-CH_2}{\underset{\displaystyle H_2\overset{..}{N}-CH_2}{\Big\backslash \quad \mid}} \qquad Me_3Si \overset{\displaystyle CH_2-CH_2}{\underset{\displaystyle \bar{O}-C=O}{\Big\backslash \quad \mid}}$$

Expanded-octet bonding would be expected to decrease the base strength of the amine by coordination of the basic nitrogen with the silicon atom. In fact, the above amine is a stronger base than *n*-propylamine.[18] The acid strength of the acid corresponding to the anion above would be expected to be increased by chelation of the carboxylate anion with the silicon. In fact, that acid is weaker than propionic acid.[19]

Triptych silicon compounds

In the discussion just concluded, the infrared spectrum of compound I-4 provides clear evidence for chelation or coordination of formally trivalent boron with carbonyl oxygen within the acetylacetonate molecule. This is not too surprising in view of the existence of stable etherates such as $BF_3 \cdot Et_2O$.

Although the simple borates, $(RO)_3B$, do not ordinarily complex with amines to any significant extent, evidence has been found for bonding between borate boron and amino nitrogen in a special ring system which constrains the two atomic centers in a position favorable for intramolecular donor-acceptor

[18] L. H. Sommer and J. Rockett, *J. Am. Chem. Soc.*, **73**, 5130 (1951).

[19] L. H. Sommer, J. R. Gold, G. Goldberg, and N. S. Marans, *J. Am. Chem. Soc.*, **71**, 1509 (1949).

interaction. Thus, H. C. Brown[20] has reported that the second-order rate constants for triethanolamine (I), $(HOCH_2CH_2)_3N$, and triethanolamine borate (II), $B(OCH_2CH_2)_3N$, with methyl-iodide in an acetonitrile solvent at $25°$, to give the quaternary ammonium compounds, are: I, 1.51×10^{-4} l. mole^{-1} sec.$^{-1}$; II, 8.57×10^{-8} l. mole^{-1} sec.$^{-1}$. The energy of activation for reaction of II exceeds that for I by 5.5 kcal./mole. For comparison, the rate constants for triethylamine and quinuclidine are 3.29×10^{-2} and 1.88 l. mole^{-1} sec.$^{-1}$, respectively. For this latter pair, conversion of acyclic nitrogen to bridgehead nitrogen gives a rate increase of a factor of about 60 (F-strain is lower for reaction of the latter), whereas, as had been noted, the corresponding change resulting in triethanolamine borate gave a large decrease in rate. The structural inference from these facts is supported by data on the reactions of triethanolamine borate with strong acids. Thus triethanolamine (like other ordinary amines having an unshared electron-pair on nitrogen) is easily titrated with hydrochloric acid in water, with perchloric acid in glacial acetic acid, or with methanesulfonic acid in nitrobenzene. In sharp contrast, at $25°$ a solution which was 0.025 M in triethanolamine borate and methanesulfonic acid (nitrobenzene solvent) required 32.5 minutes for 50% neutralization. With HCl in water, the half-time for neutralization of triethanolamine borate was 1,624 sec. In glacial acetic acid, titration of the same amine required 220 sec. for half-neutralization with perchloric acid. These facts may be summarized by the statement that the presence of borate-boron severely decreases the availability of the "lone pair" on the tertiary nitrogen in triethanolamine borate, and lead to the postulate of transannular bonding and a "triptych" structure for this compound.[20] Additional supporting evidence for transannular bonding comes from a quantitative study of the hydrolysis of triisopropanolamine borate which showed greatly decreased rates of reaction at the boron atom; the latter should be less electrophilic as a consequence of such bonding.[21]

There are some chemical points of similarity between the carbon of a carbonyl group (which is, of course, unsaturated) and a tetravalent silicon atom, and it is, therefore, of some

[20] H. C. Brown and E. A. Fletcher, *J. Am. Chem. Soc.*, **73**, 2808 (1951).

[21] H. Steinberg and D. L. Hunter, *J. Am. Chem. Soc.*, **82**, 853 (1960).

interest to discuss briefly the evidence for transannular donor-acceptor bonding between N and C_{CO}. N. J. Leonard and co-workers have contributed significant studies in this area, and the following discussion closely parallels their treatment.

For rings incorporating both a ketone and an amino function, it was found that transannular interaction is especially indicated for eight-, nine-, and ten-membered rings in which a full trans-annular bond between N and C_{CO} can produce five- or six-membered rings within the larger cycle.[22] Infrared studies of the change in carbonyl frequency with ring size, and of the N—H and O—H bond-stretching frequency range in the perchlorates of the aminoketones, support the conclusions.[22] Later studies on the electric dipole moments of various cyclic aminoketones, as well as other evidence, showed significant transannular inter-action in 11-methyl-11-azabicyclo[5,3,1]hendecane-4-one. The dipole moment data were interpreted to indicate 11 to 12%

charge separation of the type: $-\overset{+}{\underset{|}{N}}-\overset{|}{\underset{|}{C}}-\bar{O}$ (ref. 23).

In 1961, C. L. Frye and coworkers reported[24] the synthesis of monomeric crystalline compounds from the reactions of tri-ethanolamine with various trialkoxysilanes:

$$ZSi(OR)_3 + (HOCHRCH_2)_3N \longrightarrow ZSi(OCHRCH_2)_3N + 3ROH$$

From the method used to prepare these compounds (which would ordinarily be expected to yield polymeric products owing to the high functionality in both reactants), and from their properties, as discussed below, it was concluded that these substances have a triptych structure.[24]

The triptych silicon compounds have melting points which range from 100 to 256°, and generally resemble the triptych boron compound in physical properties. Furthermore, the silicon compounds, like the boron compound, are reported to be slowly neutralized by perchloric acid in a glacial acetic acid medium—

[22] N. J. Leonard, R. C. Fox, M. Oki, and S. Chiavarelli, *J. Am. Chem. Soc.*, **76**, 630 (1954).

[23] N. J. Leonard, D. F. Morrow, and M. T. Rogers, *J. Am. Chem. Soc.*, **79**, 5476 (1957).

[24] C. L. Frye, G. E. Vogel, and J. A. Hall, *J. Am. Chem. Soc.*, **83**, 996 (1961).

Table 1-3
Si—H stretching frequency in triptych and
related compounds

Compound	ν(SiH), cm.$^{-1}$
HSi(OCH$_3$)$_3$	2203 (CCl$_4$)
	2201 (piperidine)
	2202 (pyridine)
HSi(OCH$_2$CH$_3$)$_3$	2196 (CCl$_4$)
HSi[OCH(CH$_3$)$_2$]$_3$	2191 (CCl$_4$)
HSi(OCH$_2$CH$_2$)$_3$N	2136 (HCCl$_3$)
	2117 (CH$_3$OH)
HSi(C$_6$H$_5$)$_3$	2126 (CCl$_4$)
HSi(CH$_2$CH$_3$)$_3$	2097 (CCl$_4$)

although no quantitative data were given. In addition, infrared studies were made of the position of the Si—H stretching frequency in the triptych compounds as compared to simpler acyclic systems. For transannular bonding between N and C$_{CO}$, the carbonyl frequency was shifted toward lower values. For Si—H, pertinent data are given in Table 1-3 as reported by Frye.

In attempting to evaluate the *extent* of transannular bonding, in the so-called "triptych" silicon compounds, we are faced with the difficulty of sparse data as reported in a communication. However, it would seem that the data in Table 1-3 indicate a far from complete contribution of the dipolar form to the ground-state structure, in the designated solvents. Instead, transannular bonding seems to occur to approximately the extent represented by the electron density at the silicon atom in HSi(C$_6$H$_5$)$_3$ and HSi(CH$_2$CH$_3$)$_3$. A. L. Smith[25] has reported accurate values for the stretching frequency of Si—H in a wide variety of compounds, and has found, in general, that the effects of substituents on ν-(SiH) are additive, and that electronegative substituents shift the frequency toward higher values. Thus, the shift toward lower frequency for Si—H in HSi(OCH$_2$CH$_2$)$_3$N relative to HSi(OCH$_2$CH$_3$)$_3$, 60 cm.$^{-1}$, is no doubt indicative of some transannular interaction, but the magnitude of the shift does not seem in accord with the existence of a full transannular bond. No doubt, it will eventually be found that the extent of transan-

[25] A. L. Smith and N. C. Angelotti, *Spectrochim. Acta,* **15,** 412 (1959).

nular bonding in the triptych silicon compounds is solvent-dependent, and, indeed, Frye and coworkers report association for these substances (high molecular weights) in toluene but not in acetonitrile. However, these data do not necessarily prove a larger extent of transannular bonding in the less polar solvent, since the better ionizing solvent should be less favorable for association of the dipolar form: $\overset{-}{Si}—\overset{+}{N}$. It may be noted again that Leonard and coworkers claim only 11 to 12% contribution of the dipolar form for cyclic aminoketones of favorable structure. In sum, it seems to the present author that all three types of transannular interaction may reasonably be regarded as involving a significant, but perhaps incomplete dative covalent bond. (However, in the crystal, as compared to solutions of these substances, crystal forces may greatly modify the contribution of the dipole form.) Finally, replacement of one of the oxygen atoms linked to silicon in the triptych structure by a methylene group leads to fast neutralization rates which indicate a considerable decrease in the extent of transannular bonding.[26] Thus we have again an indication of the critical dependence of σ-bonding involving silicon's $3d$ orbitals on the presence of highly electronegative groups attached to that atom.

Complexes of silicon halides with amines

From previous discussion it might be anticipated that SiF_4 would be an ideal silicon halide for forming complexes with tertiary amines via expanded-octet σ-bonding. In fact, two such complexes with trimethylamine are known and well characterized. Table 1-4 summarizes some of the properties of these interesting complexes.[27] Thus it is seen that the two complexes are remarkably similar in their properties. This conclusion is reinforced by the dissociation pressure data[27] in Table 1-5. The complex $Me_3N \cdot HSiF_3$, as briefly described by Burg,[28] is formed without residues, and its dissociation pressure is measured as

[26] C. L. Frye, private communication.

[27] C. J. Wilkens and D. K. Grant, *J. Chem. Soc.*, 927 (1953).

[28] A. B. Burg, in J. H. Simons, "Fluorine Chemistry," vol. I, Academic Press Inc., New York, 1950, pp. 108–109.

Table 1-4
Trimethylamine–silicon tetrafluoride complexes

Compound	$SiF_4 \cdot NMe_3{}^a$	$SiF_4 \cdot 2NMe_3$
Melting point, deg.	81.5	89
Sublimation point, deg.	63.5	63
Latent heat of sublimation, kcal./mole	13.7	13.9

[a] Vapor density measurements indicate at least 91% dissociation in the vapor phase at 42.1° in the absence of a solid phase.

24 mm. at 0°. Turning to organosilicon fluorides, we find that the sole example reported is $Me_3N \cdot SiMeF_3$, for which the reported dissociation pressure[29] is 11.7 mm. at $-70.5°$. The remarkable drop in stability engendered by the presence of one methyl group in the last complex is noteworthy in that it cannot be attributed solely to the unfavorable steric effect of methyl relative to H or F. The situation is much more complex as indicated by a reported[29] dissociation pressure of 23 mm. at 0° for $Me_3N \cdot SiClF_3$; Cl and Me have closely similar steric requirements.

Turning now to a significant series of studies on the complexes of trimethylamine with the family $SiCl_xH_{4-x}$ by Burg,[30] we find further indications of complex structure-stability relationships for these complexes: (1) No evidence could be obtained for the formation of a 1:2 complex with any of the chlorosilanes, i.e., $(SiCl_xH_{4-x}) \cdot 2NMe_3$ is not formed. (2) 1:1 complexes are formed by $SiCl_4$ and $SiCl_2H_2$: $SiCl_3H$ and $SiClH_3$ undergo trimethylamine-catalyzed disproportionation into other chlorosilanes. (3) SiH_4 forms no complex at the temperatures investigated (down to at least $-80°$). (4) The complexes formed with $SiCl_4$

[29] J. E. Ferguson, D. K. Grant, R. H. Hickford, and C. J. Wilkens, *J. Chem. Soc.*, 99 (1959).

[30] A. B. Burg, *J. Am. Chem. Soc.*, **76**, 2694 (1954).

Table 1-5
Dissociation pressures of SiF_4NMe_3 complexes

Temperature, °C.	0	20.75	35	62.85
$p_{mm.}$, $SiF_4 \cdot NMe_3$	6.5	38.2	113.2	727
$p_{mm.}$, $SiF_4 \cdot 2NMe_3$	6.3	37.5	113.2	750

and SiH_2Cl_2 give temperature–dissociation pressure data which follow equations of the form log $p_{mm.} = a - b/T$ with excellent precision: complete dissociation into the silicon halide and Me_3N in the vapor phase is indicated and the complexes are solids. (5) The $SiCl_4$ and SiH_2Cl_2 complexes have dissociation pressures of 3.87 mm./$-56.2°$ and 28.7 mm./$25.0°$, respectively. In connection with the formation of complexes between Me_3N and organosilicon chlorides, it is of considerable interest to note the report[29] that $MeSiCl_3$ forms no complex at $-95°$.

If we seek data on the stability of complexes of Me_3N with substances whose acceptor properties are definitely known to result from their ability to undergo expansion of the covalence or coordination number of the central atom, we find extensive pressure-temperature data for $Me_3N \cdot R_3B$. In particular, $Me_3N \cdot Me_3B$ is a white sublimable solid which crystallizes from the vapor phase as long colorless needles, has a melting point of 128°, and yields the following saturation pressure data (for equilibria between vapor and solid phases):[31] 0.24 mm./0.0°, 2.00 mm./24.2°, and 25.8 mm./55.8°. Dissociation pressure measurements on the unsaturated vapor (no solid phase) gave the following degrees of dissociation in the vapor α at the designated temperature:[31] 0.638/65.8°, 0.797/80.0°, and 0.920/99.0°. Even after taking into account the nearly complete dissociation of the silicon halide Me_3N complexes in the vapor and the appreciably incomplete dissociation of the boron complex, it is clear that comparison of the dissociation pressure data for the most stable complexes of the former (i.e., SiF_4 and SiH_2Cl_2) with saturation pressure data for the latter at room temperature indicates far greater stability for $Me_3N \cdot Me_3B$. Of itself, the fact of complete or nearly complete dissociation of the silicon halide complexes in the vapor is significant and receives additional comment below. In view of the smaller covalent radius of boron (0.79 Å.) relative to silicon (1.18 Å.) and the probable large influence of steric factors on these equilibria as reported by Brown and coworkers (F-strain)[31] for the substances $Me_3N \cdot R_3B$, it would appear that we have here further evidence that the acceptor capacity of formally trivalent boron greatly exceeds that of formally tetravalent silicon, even in the very favorable

[31] H. C. Brown, H. Bartholomay, and M. D. Taylor, *J. Am. Chem. Soc.,* **66,** 435 (1944).

case of SiF_4, provided that the trimethylamine–silicon halide complexes really involve expanded-octet σ-bonding. On this latter point the possibility that the $Me_3N \cdot SiF_4$ complex has an ionic structure, $[Me_3N—SiF_3]^+F^-$, has been proved incorrect by the finding[29] that the molten complex has an exceedingly low specific conductivity, 1.4×10^{-3} ohm^{-1} cm.$^{-1}$.

By a significant and very thorough series of experiments, Wannagat and Schwarz[32] have unequivocally demonstrated that carefully dried pyridine reacts with certain pure silicon halides in ether or benzene solution to give complexes of the composition SiX_4Py_2. These complexes are formed from SiF_4, $SiCl_4$, $SiBr_4$, and $SiHCl_3$ with considerable evolution of heat. Turning to organosilicon chlorides, it was found that complexes are *not* formed by $MeSiCl_3$, Me_2SiCl_2, and Me_3SiCl.

The SiX_4Py_2 complexes are white powders which cannot be recrystallized from organic solvents and react violently with water. Although they are crystalline, as indicated by Debye-Scherrer lines, they do not melt, but instead undergo decomposition into their components which recombine in an apparent sublimation process. This behavior, as well as their complete lack of solubility in toluene, benzene, ether, dioxane, and chloroform, is certainly not characteristic of simple covalently bonded substances. Nevertheless, infrared and x-ray studies have provided evidence that the structures of $GeCl_4Py_2$ and $SiCl_4PY_2$ (the latter has an infrared spectrum virtually identical with the former, which was actually studied by x-ray diffraction) are centrosymmetric, have octahedral form, and do not contain ionic Cl. In fact, the evidence is fairly convincing that $SiCl_4Py_2$ has a *trans*-dipyridinetetrachlorosilane octahedral structure, in which the pyridine molecules occupy the two apical, and the chlorines the four equatorial positions.[33]

Wannagat and Schwarz[32] also reported the significant observation that, in sharp contrast to pyridine, the following amines do *not* give complexes with SiF_4, $SiCl_4$, $SiBr_4$, and $SiHCl_3$: quinoline; 2-methylpyridine; 2,4,6-trimethylpyridine; acridine. This remarkable dependence of complex stability on the molecular shape of the amine plus the fact that $SiBr_4$ forms a complex with pyridine, despite the large steric requirements of Br groups,

[32] U. Wannagat and R. Schwarz, *Z. Anorg. Allgem. Chem.*, **277**, 73 (1954).

[33] R. Hulme, G. J. Leigh, and I. R. Beattie, *J. Chem. Soc.*, 366 (1960).

the failure of the complexes to yield a stable liquid phase on heating, and the insolubility of the complexes in solvents such as chloroform, are all indicative of strong electrostatic forces which hold the molecules in specific orientations in the crystals and give the complexes saltlike properties. Thus, the molecules probably have large dipole moments resulting from formal charge separation of the type $C_5H_5\overset{+}{N}-\overset{=}{Si}(Cl_4)-\overset{+}{N}C_5H_5$. As the size of the amine molecules is increased or their shape is altered, the separation of the dipoles in the crystals may be increased on account of steric repulsions or other factors, and this would lead, in turn, to decreased crystal energy and decreased stability. If crystal energies contribute significantly to the stabilities of the pyridine complexes, it is not surprising to find no complex formation with bases such as quinoline. Furthermore, an important contribution of crystal energy to the stability of the trimethylamine–silicon halide complexes previously discussed might invalidate any quantitative conclusions concerning the effect of structure on complex stability in terms of the strengths of expanded-octet σ-bonding in the various complexes. However, the data probably have semiquantitative significance because the groups attached to silicon in these complexes are monatomic, with the exception of the methyl halosilanes whose methyl groups are about the same size as Cl.

There are two further aspects of the work of Wannagat and Schwarz[32] which are noteworthy: (1) None of the pyridine-type bases mentioned above reacted with CI_4; (2) SiI_4 in benzene solution reacted with all the pyridine-type bases mentioned to give structures containing four molecules of base per molecule of SiI_4. Substances of the type SiI_4Py_4 are yellow-orange in color (SiX_4Py_2 is white), and their sensitivity to moisture (despite the great ease of hydrolysis of SiI_4 itself) is far less than that of SiX_4Py_2. The SiI_4 complexes show no melting point; they decompose above 100° with increasing darkening. The fact that even 2,4,6-trimethylpyridine gives an SiI_4base_4 complex is evidence that the postulate of an ionic structure[32] $[SiPy_4]^{4+}4[I]^-$ may be valid. However, definitive evidence for such a structure is certainly necessary.

We may conclude this discussion of amine complexes by noting that, on balance, the evidence seems good that these structures involve (roughly speaking) sp^3d bonding of the Si in substances such as $SiF_4 \cdot Me_3N$ and sp^3d^2 bonding of the Si in substances such as $SiF_4 \cdot 2Me_3N$, but that crystal energies probably play a significant role in stabilizing the complexes.[34] Furthermore, the acceptor capacity of formally tetravalent silicon does not seem to match that of formally trivalent boron. Also, for purposes of future discussion, it is important to note that $MeSiF_3$ forms a very unstable complex with Me_3N while $MeSiCl_3$ forms no complex at all with trimethylamine or pyridine.

1-6   Bond energy, bond refraction, and bond polarity

Before listing values for the bond energies of pertinent linkages of carbon and silicon, it is important to note the following: (1) For polyatomic molecules thermochemical data furnish a value for the *total* energy of dissociation into atoms, i.e., for the sum of the bond energies in the molecule, but not for the individual bond energies.   Thus each bond-energy value represents the average amount of energy needed to break all the bonds. (2) The bond-energy values are so chosen that their sums represent the enthalpy changes $(-\Delta H)$ at $25°$ accompanying the formation of molecules from atoms, all in the gas phase.   (3) The spectrographic atomic ground states are chosen as the simplest and most accessible reference points, despite the fact that it would be better, from a theoretical standpoint, to use the bond energies referred to the gaseous atoms in the electronic configuration corresponding to the appropriate type of bonding.   (4) The calculation of bond energies depends upon accurate enthalpies (at $25°$) of monatomic gases of the elements relative to their standard states, and these enthalpy values are not easily determined in some cases.   Thus, Pauling[35] prefers the NBS value[36] of 88.04 kcal./mole for silicon, whereas Cottrell[37] has chosen

---

[34] The possibility of halogen bridging in the formally pentavalent-silicon amine complexes has been raised,[29] but definitive evidence for this postulate is not available at present.

[35] L. Pauling, "The Nature of the Chemical Bond," 3d ed., Cornell University Press, Ithaca, N.Y., 1960, pp. 85–86.

[36] F. Rossini, D. D. Wagman, W. H. Evans, S. Levine, and I. Jaffe, *Nat. Bur. Std. Circ.*, 500, Government Printing Office, Washington, D.C., 1952.

[37] T. Cottrell, "The Strength of Chemical Bonds," 2d ed., Butterworth & Co. (Publishers), Ltd., London, 1958, pp. 270–280.

Table 1-6
Bond energies for certain linkages of silicon and carbon[a,b] (kcal./mole)

Bond no.	Silicon bond	Bond energy	Carbon bond	Bond energy
1	Si—Si	42–53	C—Si	69–76
2	Si—C	69–76	C—C	83–83
3	Si—H	70–76	C—H	99–99
4	Si—O	88–108	C—O	84–86
5	Si—F	129–135	C—F	105–111
6	Si—Cl	86–91	C—Cl	79–81
7	Si—Br	69–74	C—Br	66–68
8	Si—I	51–56	C—I	58–51

[a] In each bond-energy entry, the first value is the Pauling bond energy, and the second that given by Cottrell.

[b] Some reported bond dissociation energies by electron impact [W. C. Steele, L. D. Nicholas, and F. G. A. Stone, *J. Am. Chem. Soc.*, 84, 4441 (1962)] are: Si—H, 94 kcal./mole; Si—Cl, 106 kcal./mole; Si—C, 79–95 kcal./mole.

105 kcal./mole for the most probable enthalpy of gaseous silicon atoms at 25°; other more minor differences in combination with the one for silicon lead to the ranges of bond-energy values listed in Table 1-6.

If, for purposes of the present discussion, we take the arithmetic mean of the two values for each bond energy and then calculate the differences for corresponding silicon and carbon bonds, $\Delta = (Si—Y) - (C—Y)$, we obtain the following values, proceeding in order from bond number 1 to 8: -25, -11, -26, $+13$, $+21$, $+9$, $+5$, -1. If we now arrange these differences in the order of increasing positive values, we find that this corresponds to an order for Y of $H < Si < C < I < Br < Cl < O < F$, and the most stable bond of silicon relative to carbon is Si—F, while the least stable is Si—H. It is clear that, roughly speaking, the bonds between silicon and highly electronegative atoms are more stable than the corresponding bonds of carbon, whereas the reverse is true for attached atoms less electronegative than iodine.

From consideration of the variation in bond-energy values with electronegativity of the attached atom, as anticipated qualitatively from periodic table and other relationships, Pauling was led to the formulation of a quantitative electronegativity scale, which is based on the postulate that the increased bond energy for linkages between unlike atoms, $D(A—B)$, over that calculated on the basis of the geometric mean for $D(A—A)$ and $D(B—B)$, is due to the extra ionic bond energy engendered by the partial ionic character of bond A—B. In detail, the difference between $D(A—B)$ and the geometric mean for $D(A—A)$ and $D(B—B)$, Δ', is not itself used for the calculation of electronegativity values. Instead, $0.18\sqrt{\Delta'}$ is taken as a convenient measure of the electronegativity difference between A and B; the values of $x_A - x_B$ for all the available bond-energy data used H as the standard with a value $x_H = 0.00$. Finally, the electronegativity values in Table 1-7 are derived by using an additive constant, 2.05, so chosen as to give the first-row elements C to F the values 2.5 to 4.0. Concerning the values given in the same table relating to the percent ionic character (calculated from $x_A - x_B$ values) of some silicon bonds, it can be said that these are based on the use of an empirical equation formulated by Pauling which gives values in reasonable accord with electric dipole moment data for *some* molecules.

For the bonds listed in Table 1-7, referring to Table 1-6 and the Pauling bond energies, we may note a rough correspondence between electronegativity difference, $x_y - x_{Si}$, and bond energy. Thus, the order of decreasing bond energies is Si—F > Si—O,

Table 1-7
Electronegativity and bond polarity for Si—Y (ref. 38)

Y	x_y	$x_y - x_{Si}$	% Ionic Character in Si—Y[a]
Si	1.8	0.0	0
C	2.5	0.7	12
H	2.1	0.3	3
O	3.5	1.7	52
F	4.0	2.2	70
Cl	3.0	1.2	30
Br	2.8	1.0	22
I	2.5	0.7	12

[a] Calculated values based on Pauling bond energies and the Pauling equation:

Amount of ionic character $= 1 - e^{-1/4(x_A - x_B)^2}$

[38] Reference 35, pp. 88–99.

Si—Cl > Si—Br, Si—C, Si—H, Si—I > Si—Si, which is roughly the order of decreasing electronegativity differences. It is possible that some of the deviations from exact correspondence are the result of more or less π-bonding in the various Si—Y linkages. But the whole situation concerning data such as those listed in Tables 1-6 and 1-7 is so unsatisfactory from an exact quantitative standpoint that it seems inadvisable to pursue the matter further at this time.

For the discussion of structure-reactivity relationships, which comprises one of the main themes of this book, there are other structure-energy relationships, in addition to bond energy, which are pertinent. One of these is the electric polarizability of molecules and their bonds. The Lorenz-Lorentz equation, relating molar refraction R, refractive index n, molecular weight MW, density d, electric polarizability α, and Avogadro's number N, is[39]

$$R = \frac{n^2 - 1}{n^2 + 2} \frac{MW}{d} = \frac{4\pi}{3} N\alpha$$

For silicon compounds it has been possible to assign bond refraction values (related to bond polarizabilities) which may be used additively to calculate with good accuracy the molar refractions of silicon-containing molecules. These values[40] and those for corresponding carbon bonds[41] are given in Table 1-8.

The data in Table 1-8 have several interesting aspects. Perhaps the most significant is the fact that the bond refraction, and presumably also the bond polarizability, of Si—Y always exceeds that for C—Y. This probably means that the electric field of an attacking reagent induces an electric moment in Si—Y, with consequent charge separation, more easily than in C—Y, and this factor may constitute an important rate factor in comparing reaction rates of corresponding silicon and carbon bonds. [A classic case often referred to in organic chemistry is the fact that C—I is usually more reactive than C—Cl, despite the fact

[39] Cf. ref. 35, pp. 605–609, for a clear and concise discussion of electric polarizability.

[40] A. I. Vogel, W. T. Cresswell, and J. Leicester, *J. Phys. Chem.*, **58**, 174 (1954).

[41] A. I. Vogel, W. T. Cresswell, G. H. Jeffrey, and J. Leicester, *J. Chem. Soc.*, 514 (1952).

Table 1-8
Bond refractions (D Line) at 20°

Bond[a]	R_D	Bond[b]	R_D
Si—Si	5.89	C—Si	2.52
Si—C	2.52	C—C	1.30
Si—C$_{ar}$	2.93		
Si—H	3.17	C—H	1.68
Si—O	1.80	(C—O)$_{ethers}$	1.54
Si—F	1.7	C—F	1.4
Si—Cl	7.11	C—Cl	6.51
Si—Br	10.08	C—Br	9.39

[a] Taken from ref. 40.
[b] Taken from ref. 41.

that the former linkage should have very little ionic character (x_C and x_I are the same, see Table 1-7), whereas the latter should have considerable ionic character corresponding to an electronegativity difference of 0.5 (7% ionic character). However, the conclusion that bond polarizability is mainly responsible for this situation is clouded by the uncertainty introduced from consideration of the bond energies of C—I and C—Cl.]

1-7 Siliconium ions

The role of carbonium ions as important reaction intermediates is well documented, and it is therefore of interest to consider certain data which are relevant to the question of whether or not siliconium ions may have a similar importance. Discussion of evidence from reaction kinetics and stereochemistry is deferred until later, and in keeping with the general subject matter of the present chapter, we shall discuss this question under two headings: (1) the energetics of gas-phase formation of siliconium ions by electron impact, and (2) ground-state siliconium ions and ground-state carbonium ions.

The ground-state electronic structure of nonbonded silicon atoms as determined spectroscopically is $1s^2\ 2s^2\ 2p^6\ 3s^2\ 3p^2$, which, it is important to note, does not correspond to the sp^3 bonding used in molecules, i.e., . . . $3s\ 3p^3$. For such gaseous atoms, the first ionization energy needed to form Si^+ is 187.9 kcal./mole; for carbon atoms ($1s^2 2s^2 2p^2$), the first ionization energy is 259.5 kcal./mole.[42] The value for Si is close to that for B, 191.2 kcal./mole, and for Ge, 182 kcal./mole, and significantly lower than for C, by some 70 kcal./mole. The latter difference, translated into thermodynamic factors such as relative heats of formation of siliconium ions, or into rate factors, would comprise an enormous driving force for siliconium-ion formation relative to carbonium ion formation, other things being equal. (However, other things are seldom equal, and the case under discussion is no exception.)

Turning now to electron impact data relating to formation of siliconium ions from bonded silicon atoms in the mass spectrometer, we may consider first the formation of various siliconium ions from silane, SiH_4. In Table 1-9 are listed the appearance potentials AP and the standard heats of formation ($\Delta H_f = 0$ for the elements in their usual states at 25°) for siliconium ions as derived from SiH_4 by electron impact and for corresponding carbonium ions as derived from CH_4.

Before the data of Table 1-9 are discussed, it may be desirable to consider briefly some fundamentals of electron

[42] Cf. ref. 35, p. 57.

Table 1-9

Gas-phase energetics for siliconium-ion and carbonium-ion formation from SiH_4 and CH_4 (kcal./mole)

Ion	AP[a]	ΔH_f	Ion	AP[a]	ΔH_f
SiH^+	335[b]	267	CH^+	530[b]	356
SiH^+	335[c]	315 (av.)	CH_2^+	360[c]	333 (av.)
SiH_2^+	430[d]		CH_2^+	465[d]	
SiH_3^+	280[e]	213	CH_3^+	330[e]	260

[a] Data reported in electron volts were converted to kcal./mole by multiplying by the conversion factor 23.05.

[b] The processes for forming these ions may involve formation of H_2 and H.

[c] For formation of the ion and H_2.

[d] For formation of the ion and 2H.

[e] For formation of the ion and H.

impact phenomena as they relate to gas-phase energetics. The data in Table 1-9 are taken from the compilation of Field and Franklin,[43] as are also the main aspects of the following brief discussion.

If no excess energy is involved, the appearance potential of an ion AP is the heat of the reaction by which the ion is formed, and the reaction process can be treated by the usual methods employed in thermochemistry. For the reaction,

$$R_1R_2 + e \longrightarrow R_1^+ + R_2 + 2e$$

in which R_2 is a free radical, the following relation will hold:

$$AP(R_1^+) = \Delta H_{\text{reaction}} = \Delta H_f(R_1^+) + \Delta H_f(R_2) - \Delta H_f(R_1R_2)$$

and it is clear that the heat of formation of the ion is calculated from AP by

$$\Delta H_f(R_1^+) = AP(R_1^+) - \Delta H_f(R_2) + \Delta H_f(R_1R_2)$$

which requires a value for the heat of formation of the reactant substance.

The heats of formation of SiH_4 and CH_4 at 25° (from the elements in their usual states at that temperature) are not greatly different, being -14.8 and -17.9 kcal./mole, respectively,[36] and the heat of formation of a hydrogen atom H is given as 52 kcal./mole by Field and Franklin.[43]

At the time of this writing, studies are being made to determine the appearance potentials for electron impact ionization of a wide variety of organosilicon compounds. Thus far this work, which is being done in collaboration with Professor F. W. Lampe, has yielded data for the gas-phase formation of trimethylsiliconium ion, Me_3Si^+, from trimethylsilane, Me_3SiH.[44]

The appearance potential for Me_3Si^+ in the process

$$Me_3SiH + e \longrightarrow Me_3Si^+ + H + 2e$$

[43] F. H. Field and J. L. Franklin, "Electron Impact Phenomena and the Properties of Gaseous Ions," Academic Press Inc., New York, 1957.

[44] F. W. Lampe, L. H. Sommer, and G. Hess, unpublished work.

is 250 ± 4 kcal./mole, and the heat of formation of Me_3Si^+, calculated using a reported ΔH_f for Me_3SiH gas at 25° of −60 kcal./mole,[45] is 138 kcal./mole. For the formation of trimethylcarbonium ion, Me_3C^+, from isobutane,[43] the appearance potential is 267 ± 8 kcal./mole, and the heat of formation of Me_3C^+ is 184 kcal./mole. The heat of formation of isobutane gas at 25° is reported as −31.5 kcal./mole, and this value in comparison to −60 kcal./mole for the silicon analogue plus a somewhat smaller AP for Me_3Si^+ formation result in a standard heat of formation for the siliconium ion which is 46 kcal./mole lower than for the carbonium ion. However, for purposes of discussion of structure-reactivity-mechanism relationships the difference in appearance potential for the two ions is more significant. If, using the designated uncertainty ranges, we minimize this difference by choosing the lowest value for Me_3C^+ and the highest for Me_3Si^+, we are still left with an AP for the former which exceeds that for the latter by 5 kcal./mole. If this difference is real, it represents a sizable driving force for siliconium-ion formation relative to carbonium-ion formation in the gas phase, at least for comparison of Me_3Si^+ and Me_3C^+ as derived from Me_3SiH and Me_3CH.* Translated into relative free energies of activation for rate, it corresponds at 25° to a rate factor of some four powers of ten, favoring formation of Me_3Si^+. However, for ordinary chemical reactions in homogeneous solution, the relatively enormous energy factors represented by the AP of the various ions considered would, of course, give such slow rates that these could not be measured. Thus, for ordinary carbonium- or siliconium-ion reactions in solution, solvation forces are of the first importance. Nevertheless, the gas-phase data should serve to indicate, at the least, that the energetics of siliconium-ion formation relative to carbonium-ion formation are not unfavorable and, indeed, may be somewhat favorable in some cases.[46] We turn now to a discussion of what is known concerning ground-state siliconium-

---

[45] S. Tannenbaum, *J. Am. Chem. Soc.*, **76**, 1027 (1954).

* *Added in proof:* C. G. Hess, F. W. Lampe, and L. H. Sommer [*J. Am. Chem. Soc.*, **86**, 3174 (1964)] have recently reported AP for formation of Me_3Si^+ from Me_3SiY, with Y being H, CH_3, C_2H_5, iso-C_3H_7, t-C_4H_9, Cl, and Me_3Si.

[46] In a recent paper, the appearance potential for Me_3Si^+ as derived from Me_3SiH is reported as 10.9 ± 0.2 electron volts (252 kcal./mole) [B. G. Hobrock and R. W. Kiser, *J. Phys. Chem.*, **66**, 155 (1962)].

ion structures relative to the situation for carbonium-ion struc-tures, and we may begin by considering the nature of the evidence for the latter.

Highly colored stable carbonium-ion complexes are formed from triarylmethyl chlorides, Ar_3CCl, and Lewis acids such as $HgCl_2$, $SnCl_4$, and $ZnCl_2$; and these complexes have structures similar to those of stable carbonium salts such as the highly colored crystalline triarylmethyl perchlorates, which were con-vincingly shown to be ionic by Hantzsch,[47] who demonstrated that nitromethane solutions of these interesting substances con-ducted electricity about as well as solutions of tetramethyl-ammonium iodide in the same solvent. In 1902 Walden[48] ob-served that colorless triphenylmethyl bromide gave a yellow solution in liquid sulfur dioxide which was conducting. Subse-quently, quantitative studies of the extent of ionization of a number of triarylmethyl halides in liquid sulfur dioxide have been reported.[49] The values obtained were found to correlate quite well, as a function of structure, with the energy differences calculated by simple molecular orbital theory.[50] For the tri-arylmethyl chlorides examined theoretically in this way by Streitwieser, it is pertinent (for subsequent discussion) to note the large decreasing effect on experimental free energy of ioniza-tion engendered by increased delocalization (resonance) energy in the carbonium ion, relative to that of the reactant triarylmethyl chlorides. As a result of its extended conjugated system, a triarylmethyl cation has a greater resonance energy than its parent chloride, and it would be expected that as this difference in resonance energy increased, the extent of ionization would increase and the experimental free energy[51] would decrease. In Table 1-10 are given some of the reported values for reactant and carbonium-ion delocalization energies DE, positive charge on the methyl carbon in the carbonium ion δ, and experimental

[47] A. Hantzsch, *Ber.,* 2573 (1921).

[48] P. Walden, *Ber.,* **35**, 2018 (1902).

[49] P. D. Bartlett and N. N. Lichtin, *J. Am. Chem. Soc.,* **73**, 5530 (1951); N. N. Lichtin and H. Glazer, *ibid.,* 5537.

[50] A. Streitwieser, Jr., *J. Am. Chem. Soc.,* **74**, 5288 (1952).

[51] These free-energy values are not those of the true equilibrium, $R_3CCl \rightleftharpoons R_3C^+ + Cl^-$, because of extensive ion-pair association. However, the extent of dissociation of the ion-pairs to ions is expected to be constant, at least to a first approximation, for a series of closely similar structures.[49,50]

Table 1-10
Delocalization energy and structure

Compound	R_1	R_2	R_3	DE of chloride[a]	DE of carbonium ion	ΔDE	ΔF, kcal./mole	δ
A	H	H	H	6.000	7.8004	1.8004	5.49	0.308
B	H	H	$m\text{-}C_6H_5$	8.3834	10.1824	1.7990	5.61	0.308
C	$m\text{-}C_6H_5$	$m\text{-}C_6H_5$	$m\text{-}C_6H_5$	13.1502	14.9462	1.7960	6.07	0.308
D	H	H	$p\text{-}C_6H_5$	8.3834	10.2018	1.8184	4.54	0.291
E	H	$p\text{-}C_6H_5$	$p\text{-}C_6H_5$	10.7668	12.6064	1.8396	3.75	0.276
F	$p\text{-}C_6H_5$	$p\text{-}C_6H_5$	$p\text{-}C_6H_5$	13.1502	15.0080	1.8578	3.17	0.262
G		β-Naphthyldiphenyl		7.6832	9.4966	1.8134	4.80	0.295

[a] Computed as the sum of the resonance energies of the constituent aromatic rings. Values computed for the DE's are: benzene, 2.000β; biphenyl, 4.3834β; naphthalene, 3.6832β.

free energies of ionization ΔF, all as a function of structure. In the original paper, a plot of the positive ΔDE values against ΔF gave a smooth curve with a negative slope. The DE values are given in terms of the exchange integral β, and the method of calculation used the LCAO (linear combination of atomic orbitals) approximation which has been applied with much success to many aromatic organic systems. The substances in Table 1-10 have the general structure $(R_1-C_6H_4)(R_2-C_6H_4)(R_3-C_6H_4)$ $C-$.

The rather high sensitivity of ΔF to small changes in ΔDE and to the amount of positive charge on the methyl carbon δ is clearly evident from Table 1-10. For the structure change A $\longrightarrow$ F, we see that a $\Delta\Delta DE$ of 0.06β and a decrease in δ of 0.046 unit of positive charge correspond to a $\Delta\Delta F$ of -2.32 kcal./mole, which in terms of equilibrium constants at $25°$ amounts to $K_F/K_A = 50$. For the change from triphenylmethyl chloride to benzhydryl chloride, only two phenyl substituents on the methyl carbon, Streitwieser has calculated by the same method[52] that the ionization of $(C_6H_5)_2CHCl$ is about 10^{-16} that of triphenylmethyl chloride, and it has been reported that benzhydryl chloride is not measurably ionized in liquid sulfur dioxide.[53]

[52] A. Streitwieser, *Chem. Rev.*, **56**, 571 (1956); see p. 611.
[53] L. C. Bateman, E. D. Hughes, and C. K. Ingold, *J. Chem. Soc.*, 1011 (1940).

The above quantitative data, cited in support of extreme sensitivity of degree of ionization to delocalization (resonance) energy, lead to the expectation that replacement of the p-phenyl substituents in compound F by $-NMe_2$ substituents, which have long been known to release electrons strongly to an attached benzene ring via mesomeric interaction, should greatly increase ΔDE. That expectation is, of course, realized by the properties of a large class of organic dyes in which the central methyl carbon bears three phenyl substituents which, in turn, bear one or more p-NMe_2 substituents. Thus, when the colorless color base of Crystal Violet, tris-(p-dimethylaminophenyl)-carbinol is dissolved in hydrochloric acid, a deep violet solution is formed whose color is due to the presence of a chemical species in which little positive charge is localized on the methyl carbon.

The violet color of the cation results from a decrease in the spacing between its ground state and excited electronic states as engendered by light, relative to the energy level spacing for the carbinol. For the cation, this results in decreased frequency for maximum absorption and shifts the wavelength maximum into the visible.

In striking and significant contrast to the behavior of the color base of Crystal Violet on treatment with acid—which changes the spectrum from $\lambda_{max.}$ 264 and 300 mμ to $\lambda_{max.}$ 319 and 441 mμ—the silicon analogue, (p-$Me_2NC_6H_4)_3SiOH$, which has $\lambda_{max.}$ 272 mμ, gives upon treatment with three equivalents of HCl a change in spectrum which reflects only the inhibition of the strong maximum due to unprotonated dimethylaminophenyl groups. Thus, in ethanol solvent, the silicon compound merely undergoes conversion of the three basic groups to their hydrochloride derivatives.[54]

The subsequent synthesis of the silicon analogue of Crystal Violet itself, (p-$Me_2NC_6H_4)_3SiCl$, allowed further interesting comparisons to be made by Wannagat.[55] The change in electronic spectrum resulting from introduction of p-Me_2N substituents was compared for $(C_6H_5)_3SiCl$ and $(C_6H_5)_3CCl$. The results were: $(C_6H_5)_3SiCl$, $\lambda_{max.}$, $CHCl_3$, 273 mμ; (p-$Me_2NC_6H_4)_3SiCl$, $\lambda_{max.}$, $CHCl_3$, 283 mμ; $(C_6H_5)_6CCl$, $\lambda_{max.}$,

[54] H. Gilman and G. E. Dunn, *J. Am. Chem. Soc.*, **72**, 2178 (1950).

[55] U. Wannagat and F. Brandmair, *Z. Anorg. Allgem. Chem.*, **280**, 223 (1955); F. Brandmair and U. Wannagat, *ibid.*, **288**, 91 (1956).

ether, 282 mμ; Crystal Violet, $\lambda_{max.}$, CHCl$_3$, 590 mμ. Infrared spectra showed the Si—Cl frequency in (C$_6$H$_5$)$_3$SiCl and (p-Me$_2$NC$_6$H$_4$)$_3$SiCl to be 513 and 508 cm.$^{-1}$, respectively. X-ray diffraction photographs showed large differences between Crystal Violet, in which the Cl is evidently not covalently bonded, and the silicon analogue.[54] Wannagat remarks that the chemical behavior of silico–Crystal Violet is not different from that of ordinary Ar$_3$SiCl compounds, and that it is readily converted to R$_3$SiOH, R$_3$SiOMe, and R$_3$SiNH$_2$ by treatment with water, methanol, and ammonia. In final comment on this interesting work, it should be noted that attempts to prepare the perchlorate with AgClO$_4$, or the tetrafluoroborate with Ba(BF$_4$)$_2$, did not yield the hoped-for derivatives of silico–Crystal Violet in solvents such as benzene, acetonitrile, cyclohexanone, acetone, or liquid sulfur dioxide. For example, AgClO$_4$ gave the expected AgCl quite rapidly in isopropanol solvent, but removal of the solvent gave only Me$_2$NC$_6$H$_5 \cdot$ HClO$_4$ as an isolable product.

The results of an extensive series of studies have been reported[56] as indicating no significant ionization of (C$_6$H$_5$)$_3$SiCl in solvents such as acetonitrile, pyridine, pyridine-nitrobenzene, nitrobenzene–aluminum tribromide [which gave extensive "ionization" of (C$_6$H$_5$)$_3$CCl] and liquid sulfur dioxide. Also, silico–Crystal Violet was found to be unionized by pyridine and nitrobenzene–aluminum tribromide. Furthermore, (C$_6$H$_5$)$_3$GeCl is unionized in acetonitrile, and (C$_6$H$_5$)$_3$SnCl is unionized in pyridine, the only solvents investigated for these chlorides. The method used was a conductimetric one, and, as is pointed out by the authors, the small values obtained for the specific conductances of the silicon, germanium, and tin chlorides may or may not be due in large part to traces of impurities in the solvents and/or the chlorides. 1296411

The general conclusion to be drawn from the foregoing electron impact and ionization data for analogous silicon and carbon compounds would appear to be that the special stability conferred upon the cations derived from aralkyl organic chlorides, due to increased delocalization (resonance) energy, does not obtain for phenyl-silicon compounds, but that the stabilities of trialkylsiliconium ions and trialkylcarbonium ions as reaction intermediates may be comparable, at least in some cases.

[56] A. B. Thomas and E. G. Rochow, *J. Inorg. Nucl. Chem.*, 4, 205 (1957).

Furthermore, when comparing analogous silicon and carbon compounds, we must not conclude that an unfavorable equilibrium constant for ionization in an equilibrium system necessarily means an unfavorable rate constant for siliconium-ion formation in a nonreversible reaction system. An equilibrium constant is, of course, the *ratio* of the forward and backward rate constants and there are many examples of nonparallel structure-equilibrium and structure-rate relationships.

The failure of silico–Crystal Violet to ionize is likely part of the general problem of why silicon does not readily engage in multiple bonding of the p_π-p_π type in its ground-state compound structures.[57] To this question we may first give the (obvious) answer that the single-bonded structures represent an energy (or free energy) advantage. Although obvious, this first answer brings the problem into sharper focus and the real problem is then seen to be one of relative energetics. For example, it cannot be concluded that a charge-delocalized structure for the (hypothetical) silico–Crystal Violet cation would have a higher energy (or free energy) than that for the real Crystal Violet cation; although this may well be the case (*vide infra*). Instead, all we really know from a completely rigorous standpoint is that the *change* from covalent to cationic structure is favored energetically for the Crystal Violet structure in an equilibrium situation. The relative ionization constants for the silicon and carbon compounds are a function of the energies of at least four structures, and these energies probably depend upon a complex of factors which may include: (1) relative steric compression (or nonbonded group repulsions) in the reactant states, expected to be less in the silicon compounds; (2) relative overlap integrals or energies for $3p_\pi$-$2p_\pi$ as compared to $2p_\pi$-$2p_\pi$ bonding in the product states; (3) the presence of a filled L electron shell in silicon but not in carbon (inner-shell repulsion energies),[58] (4) the Si—Cl compared to the C—Cl bond energy; (5) d_π-p_π bonding in Si—Cl but not in C—Cl; (6) other factors.

A recent report[59] claims that the reaction of Ph_3SiI with

---

[57] This does not mean that p_π-p_π bonding in transition-state structures is impossible for silicon, although evidence for such transition states is as yet unavailable.

[58] K. S. Pitzer, *J. Am. Chem. Soc.*, **70**, 2140 (1948).

[59] J. Y. Corey and R. West, *J. Am. Chem. Soc.*, **85**, 4043 (1963).

2,2'-bipyridine in methylene chloride solvent yields a penta-coordinate-siliconium ion in which the silicon is bonded to three phenyl groups and two nitrogens. Since this is a preliminary report and the structure of the isolated substance has not been clearly demonstrated, no further comment is made here.

1-8   Organosilyl free radicals and silanions

It is interesting to note here that the mono- and disilicon analogues of hexaphenylethane, Ph_3SiCPh_3 and $Ph_3SiSiPh_3$, in contrast to the carbon compound, show no tendency to dissociate into radicals when in solution, do not react with oxygen or other oxidizing agents such as selenium dioxide and lead tetraacetate, and also do not react with iodine in boiling xylene.[60] In this connection it is of interest to note again the low bond energy of the Si—Si bond,* 42 to 53 kcal./mole, compared to that for C—C, 83 kcal./mole (Table 1-6). Thus, a favorable delocalization (resonance) energy factor for the triphenylmethyl radical compared to that for a triphenylsilyl radical is indicated as one critical factor; another may be the larger phenyl-phenyl repulsion energies in the react-ant carbon structure. The stereochemistry of substitution at silicon by free-radical processes is as yet unknown, and this subject is not dealt with in later pages. Fundamental structural data are not yet available for silanions.[61]

[60] Cf. T. C. Wu and H. Gilman, *J. Org. Chem.,* **23,** 913 (1958), and refer-ences cited therein.

[61] For an excellent review of organosilylmetallic chemistry (Ph_3SiK, Ph_3SiLi, etc.) see H. Gilman and H. J. S. Winkler, in H. Zeiss, "Organometallic Chemistry," Reinhold Publishing Corporation, New York, 1960, chap. 6.

* *Added in proof:* The bond dissociation energy by electron impact has recently been reported as being 81 kcal./mole for Si—Si in $Me_3SiSiMe_3$: C. G. Hess, F. W. Lampe, and L. H. Sommer, *J. Am. Chem. Soc.,* **86,** 3174 (1964).

chapter two **Optically active compounds**

2-1 Synthesis of optically active α-NpPhMeSiX compounds (R₃Si*X)

The presently available detailed knowledge of the stereochemistry of substitution at saturated carbon atoms, which had its start with the discovery of the Walden Inversion[1] in 1895, stands in sharp contrast to the complete lack of information concerning the stereochemistry of substitution reactions at asymmetric silicon atoms which obtained until very recently. It would not be fruitful to discuss at length the causes for the general lack of research effort in this area, but it should perhaps be noted that organosilicon compounds in general are "unnatural products," and hence optically active organosilicon compounds, unlike the natural α-amino acids and α-hydroxy acids used by Walden in his classical studies, are not directly available from natural sources.

In all, resolution of three organosilicon compounds,[2,3] only two of which contained (relatively unreactive) functions bonded to asymmetric silicon, were carried out by the pioneer of organosilicon chemistry, F. S. Kipping; but the routes to the optically active compounds were so tedious and lengthy, the amounts obtained were so small, and the optical rotations so feeble, that studies of stereochemistry were not possible with these substances, which had the further serious disadvantage of sulfonic acid groups bonded to carbon. Reaction of such strongly acidic groups with reactive functions on silicon would be inevitable, and Kipping's compounds therefore seem most unsuitable for stereochemical studies on this basis alone. The condition that suitable organosilicon structures should have no reactive functional groups linked to carbon imposed the requirement that resolution be effected through separation of diastereoisomers in which the central silicon atom is directly bonded to an optically active group provided by the resolving agent. These conditions

---

[1] P. Walden, *Ber.,* **28,** 1287, 2766 (1895).

[2] F. S. Kipping and coworkers, *J. Chem. Soc.,* 209 (1917); 2090 (1908); 755 (1910).

[3] Preparation of an optically active organosilicon compound *not* having a reactive functional group on silicon, p-carboxyphenylmethylethylphenylsilane, has been reported more recently [C. Eaborn and C. Pitt, *Chem. & Ind. (London),* 830 (1958)].

were met by the synthesis and separation of $(\pm)$-α-naphthyl-phenylmethyl-$(-)$-menthoxysilanes.[4] In the following reaction scheme, $(-)$MenOH is $(-)$menthol:

$$PhMeSi(OMe)_2 \xrightarrow{\alpha\text{-NpMgBr}} (\pm)\text{-}\alpha\text{-NpPhMeSiOMe} \xrightarrow[\text{KOH}(s)]{(-)\text{MenOH}}$$

$$(\pm)\text{-}\alpha\text{-NpPhMeSiO-}(-)\text{Men} \xrightarrow[\text{pentane}\,(-78^\circ)]{\text{crystallize}}$$

$$(-)\text{-}\alpha\text{-NpPhMeSiO-}(-)\text{Men}$$

The mixture of diastereoisomers afforded by treatment of the racemic methoxysilane with $(-)$menthol, in the presence of solid KOH as a catalyst, is a viscous syrup which, however, readily gives an excellent yield (92%) of the higher-melting less soluble diastereoisomer when dissolved in pentane and chilled to -78°. This nicely crystalline substance has m.p. 82–84° and $[\alpha]_D - 53.9^\circ$ (c 11.32, cyclohexane). The more soluble diastereoisomer which is also lower melting has m.p. 56.5–59° and $[\alpha]_D -47^\circ$ (c 1.40, cyclohexane), and requires several recrystallizations to free it from admixture with the higher-melting diastereoisomer.

Treatment of the higher-melting diastereoisomer which is *levorotatory* with lithium aluminum hydride furnished a *dextrorotatory* product after removal of the formed $(-)$menthol, and thus showed at once that separation of diastereoisomers had indeed been effected by fractional crystallization from pentane; that reduction of menthoxysilanes with lithium aluminum hydride is stereospecific, at least to some degree; and, finally, and most important of all, that *stereospecific substitutions at asymmetric silicon can be realized.*[4,5] The significance of the last statement is placed in proper perspective by the realization that *no* stereospecific reactions of asymmetric silicon were known before the carrying out of this experiment.

$$(-)\text{-}\alpha\text{-NpPhMeSiO-}(-)\text{Men} \xrightarrow{\text{LiAlH}_4} (+)R_3Si^*H$$
$$[\alpha]_D -53.9^\circ \qquad\qquad [\alpha]_D +33.4^\circ$$

The product R_3Si^*H had m.p. 61.5–63°, and was obtained in 91% yield. The reduction was at least 94% stereospecific (see

[4] L. H. Sommer and C. L. Frye, unpublished work; see C. L. Frye, Ph.D. Thesis, The Pennsylvania State University, 1960.

[5] L. H. Sommer and C. L. Frye, *J. Am. Chem. Soc.*, **81,** 1013 (1959).

below). The lower-melting diastereoisomer gave *levorotatory* R_3Si^*H when reduced with lithium aluminum hydride. This product had m.p. 63–64°, $[\alpha]_D$ −32.8°, after several recrystallizations from pentane.

Treatment of the higher-melting diastereoisomer with boron trifluoride etherate furnished optically active fluorosilane in a reaction at least 90% stereospecific.[4,6]

$$(-)\text{-}\alpha\text{-NpPhMeSiO-}(-)\text{Men} \xrightarrow{\text{BF}_3 \cdot \text{Et}_2\text{O}} (-)R_3Si^*F$$
$$[\alpha]_D \ -53.9° \qquad\qquad\qquad\qquad [\alpha]_D \ -40.9°$$

Recrystallization of the product yielded a purer product having $[\alpha]_D$ −46.9° and m.p. 67.5–68°. Purification of optically active R_3Si^*H and R_3Si^*F by fractional crystallization is easily accomplished because their racemic modifications comprise lower-melting more soluble eutectics.

Because of the long-standing and continuing interest in the stereochemistry of substitution of organic chlorides, the next objective related to the synthesis of optically active organosilicon chlorides in order that the stereochemistry of substitution of this important class of organosilicon compounds might become known, and thereby permit comparison with analogous reactions of organic chlorides. From reported data on the reactions of inactive organosilicon hydrides with chlorine[7] and iodine[8] it seemed clear that these reactions might follow heteropolar rather than homopolar mechanisms, and this raised the possibility of stereospecific chlorination of optically active R_3Si^*H. Reaction of the latter with chlorine is rapid in the presence or absence of light and shows a marked dependence of rate on the nature of the solvent; in agreement with the observations reported by Russell,[7] rates are fast in CCl_4 and much slower in cyclohexane solvent.

Chlorination of *dextrorotatory* R_3Si^*H in CCl_4 solvent gave an optically active chlorosilane, and the latter was reduced by lithium aluminum hydride in ether to *levorotatory* R_3Si^*H.[5]

$$(+)R_3Si^*H \xrightarrow[(1)]{\text{Cl}_2} (-)R_3Si^*Cl \xrightarrow[(2)]{\text{LiAlH}_4} (-)R_3Si^*H$$
$$[\alpha]_D \ +34° \qquad\quad [\alpha]_D \ -6.3° \qquad\quad [\alpha]_D \ -34°$$

[6] L. H. Sommer and M. C. Musolf, unpublished work.

[7] G. A. Russell, *J. Org. Chem.*, **21**, 1190 (1956).

[8] D. R. Deans and C. Eaborn, *J. Chem. Soc.*, 3169 (1954).

From the above reaction sequence it follows at once that reactions (1) and (2) are highly stereospecific, and that one of these must proceed with essentially pure retention of configuration, and the other with essentially pure inversion of configuration.

Thus, 63 years after the discovery of the first Walden cycle for carbon, a similar cycle was discovered for silicon, and the problem of the Walden cycle, deciding which reactions in such a cycle are inversions and which retentions, emerged.

In organic chemistry, the problem of the first Walden cycle remained unsolved for at least 40 years.[9] For organosilicon stereochemistry, the process was greatly accelerated by the use of modern chemical and physical methods. The methods used for correlation of configuration are discussed in Chap. 7. For purposes of discussion of the stereochemistry of R_3Si^*X reactions, the results of the correlation are detailed in the next section.

2-2 Assignment of relative configuration

In Table 2-1 are listed the R_3Si^*X compounds which have the same configuration as $(+)R_3SiH$. Justification for these assignments of relative configuration depends, in part, on the reactions which are discussed in the next four chapters, and therefore is best deferred to Chap. 7.

2-3 Special need for stereochemical studies of compounds of second-row elements

The general problem of formulating accurate descriptions of the mechanisms of organosilicon reactions is a far from simple one. For compounds of silicon, phosphorus, and sulfur, a major complicating factor is the question of participation or nonparticipation of $3d$ orbitals in individual reactions, as a function of reactant and reagent structures and the nature of the solvent. As is evident from the preceding discussion in Chap. 1, considerable dependence of $3d$ orbital participation on these factors may be

---

[9] Cf. C. K. Ingold, "Structure and Mechanism in Organic Chemistry," Cornell University Press, Ithaca, N.Y., 1953, p. 373.

Table 2-1
Enantiomers having the $(+)R_3Si^*H$ configuration

Compound	$[\alpha]_D$, solvent[a]	m.p.
$(+)R_3Si^*H$	$+34°$, pentane	$64°$
$(-)R_3Si^*Cl$	$-6.3°$, pentane	$64°$
$(+)R_3Si^*OH$	$+20°$, ether	liq.
$(+)R_3Si^*OMe$	$+17°$, pentane	$64°$
$(-)R_3Si^*-(-)OMen$	$-59°$, cyclohexane	$84°$
$(-)R_3Si^*O-cycloC_6H_{11}$	$-8.0°$, pentane	liq.
$(-)R_3Si^*O-t-C_4H_9$	$-28°$, pentane	liq.
$(+)R_3Si^*OCOCH_3$	$+18°$, hexane	liq.
$(+)R_3Si^*OCOC_6H_5$	$+18°$, pentane	liq.
$(+)R_3Si^*OSi^*R_3$	$+9.9°$, hexane	$89°$
$(+)R_3Si^*C_2H_5$	$+6.1°$, pentane[b]	liq.
$(-)R_3Si^*Br$	$-22°$, pentane	$54°$
$(+)R_3Si^*F$	$+47°$, pentane	$68°$
$(-)R_3Si^*OK$	$-75°$, xylene	
$(+)R_3Si^*OCOC_6H_4NO_2$-p	$+22°$, ether	$130°$
$(+)R_3Si^*OCOC_6H_3(NO_2)_2-3,5$	$+24°$, ether	liq.

[a] With the exception of $R_3Si^*C_2H_5$, all the above enantiomers derive (directly or indirectly) from R_3Si^*H and can be reconverted to that substance. The reconversion to R_3Si^*H allows the above values to be given with considerable assurance that they correspond to a high level of optical purity.

[b] The value of $+6.1°$ for $R_3Si^*C_2H_5$ is simply the highest rotation obtained for this substance. Its optical purity is not known.

anticipated.   Another facet of the general problem of organosilicon mechanisms relates to the question of whether siliconium ions are important reaction intermediates.

The wholesale transfer of mechanism criteria from organic chemistry to organosilicon chemistry involves many hazards. For example, a bimolecular rate law for an organosilicon reaction does not in any way distinguish between an S_N2 mechanism and one involving an expanded-octet intermediate which obeys the steady-state approximation for unstable intermediates.   Furthermore, it cannot be assumed (as has been done in some rate studies) that the criteria which apply to S_N1 reactions in carbon chemistry should also apply to ionization reactions of organosilicon compounds.   The fine structure of R_3Si^+ may differ considerably from that of R_3C^+, especially with regard to charge delocalization.

In the next four chapters it will be shown how the use of optically active compounds reveals mechanism detail not easily available from rate studies alone.   In combination, stereochemistry and rate studies provide a powerful tool for mechanism discernment.   Without stereochemical studies, the accurate formulation of reaction mechanisms for compounds of the second-row elements is especially difficult and sometimes impossible.*

* *Added in proof:* A detailed treatment of the syntheses and correlations of configuration discussed in this chapter has been published recently: L. H. Sommer, C. L. Frye, G. A. Parker, and K. W. Michael, *J. Am. Chem. Soc.,* **86,** 3271 (1964).

chapter three **Stereochemistry and mechanisms of silicon-oxygen bonds**

3-1   Introduction

An excellent general review of the chemistry of organosilicon compounds containing Si—O bonds is available.[1] This subject is extensive and important, but fundamental rate studies of mechanism have been few in number. Such studies have been limited by the diversity of reactions available to Si—O bonds in some circumstances and by the fast rates which obtain for many reaction systems.

It seems appropriate to begin the discussion of the stereochemistry of R_3Si^*O— reactions by noting that the evidence[1] for d_π-p_π bonding in Si—O bonds is quite convincing:

$$\equiv Si\!-\!\overset{..}{\underset{..}{O}}\!:\!H \qquad \text{and} \qquad \equiv Si\!-\!\overset{..}{\underset{..}{O}}\!:\!R$$

$$\text{I} \qquad\qquad\qquad\qquad \text{II}$$

One result of d_π-p_π bonding in silanols (I) is enhanced acidity toward alkali and alkali metals, relative to analogous carbinols. (It may be noted here that increased d_π-p_π bonding must be present in the conjugate base of I, if such bonding is responsible for increased acidity.) Also, despite d_π-p_π bonding in II (alkoxides and siloxanes, e.g., R_3SiOMe and $R_3SiOSiR_3$) acid- and base-catalyzed rates for II are frequently very fast, relative to analogous organic reactions. Evidently the polarizability of such d_π-p_π bonding is quite high.

3-2   Syntheses

The conversion of R_3Si^*OH to optically active R_3Si^*OK is easily accomplished by shaking a xylene solution of the silanol with excess powdered $KOH(s)$.

$$(+)R_3Si^*OH + KOH(s) \xrightarrow{\text{xylene}} (-)R_3Si^*OK \qquad (3\text{-}1)$$
$$[\alpha]_D\ +20° \qquad\qquad\qquad [\alpha]_D\ -75°$$

[1] C. Eaborn, "Organosilicon Compounds," Butterworth & Co. (Publishers), Ltd., London, 1960, chaps. 8 and 9.

It is remarkable that the optical rotation of the xylene solution of R_3Si^*OK, in contact with excess $KOH(s)$, remains constant for long periods. Indeed, no change was observed after 6 months. Treatment of $(+)R_3Si^*OH$ with potassium metal also gives $(-)R_3Si^*OK$, but this procedure is less convenient.

Treatment of $(-)R_3Si^*OK$ with water gives back $(+)R_3Si^*OH$ in a reversal of reaction (3-1).

Reactions of R_3Si^*OK with various organic compounds are important for synthesis and also for chemical correlations of configuration (see Chap. 7). Some of these are given below:

$$(-)R_3Si^*OK + Me_2SO_4 \xrightarrow{\text{xylene}} (+)R_3Si^*OMe \qquad (3\text{-}2)$$
$$[\alpha]_D\ -75° \qquad\qquad\qquad [\alpha]_D\ +16°$$

$$(-)R_3Si^*OK + CH_3COCl \xrightarrow{\text{xylene}} (+)R_3Si^*OCOCH_3 \quad (3\text{-}3)$$
$$[\alpha]_D\ -75° \qquad\qquad\qquad [\alpha]_D\ +18°$$

$$(-)R_3Si^*OK + C_6H_5COCl \xrightarrow{\text{xylene}} (+)R_3Si^*OCOC_6H_5$$
$$[\alpha]_D\ -70° \qquad\qquad\qquad [\alpha]_D\ +18° \qquad (3\text{-}4)$$

$$(-)R_3Si^*OK + p\text{-}NO_2C_6H_4COCl \xrightarrow{\text{xylene}}$$
$$[\alpha]_D\ -70°$$
$$\qquad\qquad (+)R_3Si^*OCOC_6H_4(NO_2)\text{-}p \quad (3\text{-}5)$$
$$\qquad\qquad [\alpha]_D\ +22°$$

$$(-)R_3Si^*OK + 3,5\text{-}(NO_2)_2C_6H_3COCl \xrightarrow{\text{xylene}}$$
$$[\alpha]_D\ -70°$$
$$\qquad\qquad (+)R_3Si^*OCOC_6H_3(NO_2)_2\text{-}3,5 \quad (3\text{-}6)$$
$$\qquad\qquad [\alpha]_D\ +24°$$

All the above reactions with R_3Si^*OK were rapid at room temperature and gave excellent yields.[2]

3-3   Grignard reduction of R_3Si^*OMe: a four-center retention mechanism

In the present author's view, one of the most convincing pieces of evidence for important operation (in nonpolar media) of a

---

[2] For a review and pertinent references dealing with most of the reactions in Sec. 3-2, see L. H. Sommer, *Angew. Chem.*, **74**, 176 (1962); *ibid., Intern. Ed. Engl.*, **1**, 143 (1962). These studies were carried out by C. L. Frye and G. A. Parker.

four-center mechanism for Si—O reactions is provided by the Grignard reduction of R_3Si^*OMe. Removal of ether solvent from a solution of t-butylmagnesium chloride and R_3Si^*OMe followed by heating at 95° for 24 hours gave a 95% yield of R_3Si^*H plus isobutylene.[3]

$$(+)R_3Si^*OMe + t\text{-}C_4H_9MgCl \longrightarrow$$
$$[\alpha]_D +15°$$

$$(+)R_3Si^*H + C_4H_8 \qquad (3\text{-}7)$$
$$[\alpha]_D +27°$$

Considering the rather drastic conditions and dubious homogeneity of the reaction, an indicated stereospecificity of only 85% is not too surprising. The predominant stereochemical path is retention of configuration.

Grignard reductions of R_3Si^*O-cycloC_6H_{11} and R_3Si^*O-t-C_4H_9 are important for correlations of configuration and for the demonstration of predominant retention of configuration in all three reductions. But the yields of R_3Si^*H and the rates of reduction were much lower for the latter two substances. The slow rates undoubtedly permit the incursion of side reactions which lowered the stereospecificity.

$$(+)R_3Si^*O\text{-cyclo}C_6H_{11} + t\text{-}C_4H_9MgCl \longrightarrow$$
$$[\alpha]_D +5°$$

$$(-)R_3Si^*H + C_4H_8 \qquad (3\text{-}8)$$
$$[\alpha]_D -12°$$

$$(+)R_3Si^*O\text{-}t\text{-}C_4H_9 + t\text{-}C_4H_9MgCl \longrightarrow$$
$$[\alpha]_D +13°$$

$$(-)R_3Si^*H + C_4H_8 \qquad (3\text{-}9)$$
$$[\alpha]_D -8°$$

A retention stereochemistry for reaction (3-7), (3-8), and (3-9), plus consideration of the general mechanism for Grignard reduction of ketones, which involves a quasi six-ring transition state:

[3] L. H. Sommer and G. A. Parker, unpublished studies.

R $\overset{\delta+}{\underset{C}{\diagup}}$ R'

H $\overset{\frown}{}$ O

β C $\underset{\underset{\alpha}{C}}{\frown}$ MgX

$\longrightarrow$

$\overset{R\quad R}{\underset{H\quad OMgX}{\diagup C \diagdown}}$

+

$\overset{\diagdown}{}C{=}C\overset{\diagup}{}$

and yields the predicted optically active alcohol when an optically active halide (reducing —H attached to asymmetric β-carbon) is used to prepare the Grignard reagent, all indicate that a similar mechanism, which has been proposed before,[4] obtains for the Grignard reductions of R_3Si^*OR compounds. The difference lies in replacement of the unsaturated carbonyl carbon by a silicon atom, and the expulsion of the —OR leaving group to maintain tetravalency of the silicon in the product.

$\underset{Me\quad Me}{\overset{\displaystyle \overset{R_3}{Si}}{\underset{\displaystyle \underset{C}{H_2C \cdots \quad MgX}}{H \qquad OMe}}}$

$\longrightarrow$

R_3SiH

+

$\overset{H\qquad Me}{\underset{H\qquad Me}{\diagup C{=}C\diagdown}}$

+

MeOMgX

(3-10)

3-4   Retention reactions of R_3Si^*OR and $R_3Si^*OSi^*R_3$

Treatment of a dilute ether solution of R_3Si^*OMe with lithium aluminum hydride for 16 hours at room temperature gave optically active R_3Si^*H in high yield.[5] This is a smooth reaction which requires far less drastic conditions than (3-7).

[4] Cf. ref. 1, p. 185.

[5] For preliminary reports of most of the data in Sec. 3-4, see L. H. Sommer, C. L. Frye, M. C. Musolf, G. A. Parker, P. G. Rodewald, K. W. Michael, Y. Okaya, and R. Pepinsky, *J. Am. Chem. Soc.*, **83**, 2210 (1961); L. H. Sommer and C. L. Frye, *ibid.*, **82**, 3796 (1960).

$$(+)R_3Si^*OMe + LiAlH_4 \longrightarrow (+)R_3Si^*H \qquad (3\text{-}11)$$
$$[\alpha]_D +16° \qquad\qquad\qquad\qquad [\alpha]_D +30°$$

This reaction is about 90% stereospecific. The predominant stereochemical path is retention of configuration. It is interesting to note that sodium borohydride, which reacts rapidly with R_3Si^*Cl [see Eq. (4-16)], gives no reduction of R_3Si^*OMe even after long periods of heating in diglyme solvent. Relative to the central boron atom in BH_4^-, the aluminum in AlH_4^- is a much better center for nucleophilic attack by oxygen-containing substances. Alcohols react readily with AlH_4^-, in comparison to BH_4^-, to give $ROAlH_3^-$ species, and the present author considers it exceedingly probable that (3-11) and the alcoholysis of AlH_4^- follow similar mechanisms, i.e., have rate-controlling transition states of approximately the following structures:

Thus, Grignard reduction and lithium aluminum hydride reduction of R_3Si^*OMe both involve a four-center retention mechanism in a nonpolar medium.

When the steric requirements of the alkoxy group are increased, more drastic conditions are required for complete reduction. Thus, the cyclohexoxysilane requires a di-n-butyl ether solvent and heating at 98–140° for 5 hours to give a 68% yield of R_3Si^*H.

$$(-)R_3Si^*O\text{-cyclo}C_6H_{11} + LiAlH_4 \longrightarrow (+)R_3Si^*H \quad (3\text{-}12)$$
$$[\alpha]_D -7.5° \qquad\qquad\qquad\qquad\qquad [\alpha]_D +30°$$

The predominant stereochemistry is again retention of configuration, and the stereospecificity is again about 90%. Treatment of the t-butoxysilane with lithium aluminum hydride in di-n-butyl ether for 3 days at 95–100° gave only a small amount of reduction with predominant retention of configuration.

$$(-)R_3Si^*O\text{-}t\text{-}C_4H_9 + LiAlH_4 \longrightarrow (+)R_3Si^*H \qquad (3\text{-}13)$$
$$[\alpha]_D -26° \qquad\qquad\qquad\qquad [\alpha]_D +25°$$

Optically active silanol is reduced by lithium aluminum hydride. A 72% yield of R_3Si^*H was obtained by heating a di-n-butyl ether solution for 2 hours.

$$(+)R_3Si^*OH + LiAlH_4 \longrightarrow (+)R_3Si^*H \qquad (3\text{-}14)$$
$$[\alpha]_D +17° \qquad\qquad\qquad\qquad [\alpha]_D +27°$$

The stereochemistry is again retention with a stereospecificity of about 90%, and the mechanism clearly involves the prior formation of the siloxy–aluminum hydride species:

$$R_3Si^*OH + LiAlH_4 \longrightarrow R_3Si^*OAlH_3^-$$

followed by a rate-controlling transition state for the formation of R_3Si^*H, which can be represented as follows:

$$
\begin{array}{c}
O \\
R_3Si^* \ominus \quad AlH_2 \\
H
\end{array}
\qquad (3\text{-}15)
$$

The optically active disiloxane afforded a 42% yield of reduction product after treatment with lithium aluminum hydride for 3 days at 110–140° in di-n-butyl ether.

$$(+)R_3Si^*OSi^*R_3 + LiAlH_4 \longrightarrow (+)R_3Si^*H \qquad (3\text{-}16)$$
$$[\alpha]_D +8.5° \qquad\qquad\qquad\qquad [\alpha]_D +22°$$

The predominant stereochemistry is again retention, and the reduced stereospecificity is perhaps not too surprising in view of the drastic conditions employed.

We turn next to a consideration of some reactions of Si—O with another base which provides displacement of —OR by —OH or —O⁻K⁺. The base is KOH(s), an exceedingly reactive reagent toward Si—O bonds.

Treatment of the optically active methoxysilane with excess powdered KOH, using a xylene solvent, gave a 90% yield of

R_3Si^*OK after 45 minutes at 95°. Treatment of the potassium silanolate with water gave R_3Si^*OH.

$$(+)R_3Si^*OMe + KOH(s) \longrightarrow \xrightarrow{H_2O} (+)R_3Si^*OH \quad (3\text{-}17)$$
$$[\alpha]_D +16° \qquad\qquad\qquad\qquad [\alpha]_D +17°$$

The predominant stereochemistry is retention, and the stereospecificity is about 90%. Similar results were obtained with the cyclohexoxysilane, after a reaction time of 90 minutes, and with the t-butoxysilane after 10 hours.

$$(-)R_3Si^*O\text{-cyclo}C_6H_{11} + KOH(s) \longrightarrow \xrightarrow{H_2O}$$
$$[\alpha]_D -8.0°$$
$$(+)R_3Si^*OH$$
$$[\alpha]_D +20° \quad (3\text{-}18)$$

$$(-)R_3Si^*O\text{-}t\text{-}C_4H_9 + KOH(s) \longrightarrow \xrightarrow{H_2O} (+)R_3Si^*OH$$
$$[\alpha]_D -26° \qquad\qquad\qquad\qquad [\alpha]_D +17° \quad (3\text{-}19)$$

It should perhaps be pointed out that retention reactions (3-17), (3-18), and (3-19) involve displacement of oxygen from asymmetric silicon. Displacement of alkoxy groups from silicon with bases is well known.[1]

The reaction of optically active disiloxane, $R_3Si^*OSi^*R_3$, with $KOH(s)$ is extremely interesting from a stereochemistry standpoint. It was carried out as follows: A solution of 0.82 g. of disiloxane in 10 ml. of xylene was heated for one hour with excess powdered potassium hydroxide, 4 g., at 95°. Assuming a quantitative conversion to the potassium silanolate, the specific rotation was determined to be $[\alpha]_D -70°$ for the product.

$$(+)R_3Si^*OSi^*R_3 + KOH(s) \longrightarrow (-)R_3Si^*OK \quad (3\text{-}20)$$
$$[\alpha]_D +9.8° \qquad\qquad\qquad\qquad [\alpha]_D -70°$$

The stereospecificity is at least 95%. Hydrolysis of the silanolate from (3-20) gave $(+)R_3Si^*OH$ having $[\alpha]_D +19°$.

Reaction (3-20) is an unusual case in stereochemistry.[5] The formation of silanolate of high optical purity proves that the stereochemical course is retention of configuration. This is made clear by consideration of the reaction with the aid of Fischer projection formulas.

$$
\begin{array}{c}
\alpha\text{-Np} \\
| \\
\text{Me}-\text{Si}-\text{Ph} \\
| \\
\text{O} \\
| \\
\text{Ph}-\text{Si}-\text{Me} \\
| \\
\alpha\text{-Np} \\
[\alpha]_D\ +9.8^\circ\ \text{(I)}
\end{array}
\;+\;2\text{KOH}\;
\xrightarrow[\text{at both Si atoms}]{\text{retention}}\;
\begin{array}{c}
\alpha\text{-Np} \\
| \\
\text{Me}-\text{Si}-\text{Ph} \\
| \\
\text{OK}\quad\text{(II)} \\
+ \\
\text{OK} \\
| \\
\text{Ph}-\text{Si}-\text{Me} \\
| \\
\alpha\text{-Np}\quad\text{(III)}
\end{array}
$$

$$
\begin{array}{c}
\alpha\text{-Np} \\
| \\
\text{Me}-\text{Si}-\text{Ph} \\
| \\
\text{O} \\
| \\
\text{Ph}-\text{Si}-\text{Me} \\
| \\
\alpha\text{-Np}
\end{array}
\;+\;2\text{KOH}\;
\xrightarrow[\text{at one Si atom}]{\text{inversion}}\;
\begin{array}{c}
\alpha\text{-Np} \\
| \\
\text{Ph}-\text{Si}-\text{Me} \\
| \\
\text{OK}\quad\text{(IV)} \\
+ \\
\text{OK} \\
| \\
\text{Ph}-\text{Si}-\text{Me} \\
| \\
\alpha\text{-Np}\quad\text{(V)}
\end{array}
$$

Firstly it should be noted that optically active $(+)R_3Si^*OSi^*R_3$ must have the same configuration at both silicon atoms. Secondly, 180° rotation of structure III in the plane of the paper gives II; structures II and III are identical enantiomers, whereas IV and V are of opposite configuration. Thus, the latter combination would be racemic, R_3Si^*OK, and the experimental observation of high optical purity rules out a stereochemistry involving inversion at one silicon and retention at the other. The third possibility, inversion at both silicon atoms, which seems unlikely on simple chemical grounds [i.e., rupture of only one Si—O bond is needed to make $2R_3Si^*OK$ species, and active R_3Si^*OK is not racemized by excess KOH(s)], is ruled out by the fact that $(+)R_3Si^*OSi^*R_3$ and $(-)R_3Si^*OK$ have the same configuration at all three silicon atoms (see Table 2-1). Thus, the formation of R_3Si^*OK of high optical purity is itself convincing evidence of retention of configuration in the special case of (3-20).

A 0.35 M solution of R_3Si^*OK in xylene is readily prepared, indicating that the solubility of the silanolate in that solvent exceeds 10% (by weight). Studies on the electrical conductivity of solutions of alkali silanolates in siloxanes showed that the extent of ionization is very small.[6] Taken together, these data indicate that potassium ion has a large "affinity" for silanolate oxygen in poor ionizing solvents such as xylene. R_3Si^*OK must exist largely as "intimate" ion-pairs rather than as dissociated ions in such solvents. These considerations, plus the fact of a retention stereochemistry, suggest that a four-center mechanism obtains for (3-20), and that the rate-controlling transition state can be represented as

$$
\begin{array}{c}
\text{SiR}_3 \\
\text{O} \\
\text{R}_3\text{Si} \diamond \text{K} \\
\text{O} \\
\text{H}
\end{array}
\qquad (3\text{-}21)
$$

There is an interesting variant of (3-21) which is possible and deserves to be mentioned. It involves a quasi six-ring process and utilizes a molecule of water coordinated with the potassium ion. (KOH(s) as used contains 10 to 12% water.)

$$
\begin{array}{c}
\text{R}_3 \\
\text{Si} \\
\text{HO} \quad \text{OSiR}_3 \\
\text{K} \quad \text{H} \\
\text{O} \\
\text{H}
\end{array}
\qquad (3\text{-}22)
$$

3-5 Mechanisms of R_3Si^*OR' compounds: discussion of S_Ni-Si and S_N2-Si mechanisms

Of themselves the data discussed in the previous two sections strongly suggest the operation of quasi-cyclic four-center mechanisms for retention reactions of R_3Si^*OR' in *nonpolar solvents*. A recent report[7] provides clear evidence for retention of configuration in the intramolecular rearrangement:

---

[6] D. T. Hurd, R. C. Osthoff, and M. L. Corrin, *J. Am. Chem. Soc.,* **76,** 249 (1954).

[7] A. G. Brook and C. M. Warner, *Tetrahedron Letters,* 815 (1962).

$$R_3Si^*\!-\!\overset{\overset{\displaystyle O^\ominus}{|}}{C}Ph_2 \xrightarrow{\text{ether}} R_3Si^*O\overset{\ominus}{C}Ph_2 \qquad (3\text{-}23)$$

The mechanism of this rearrangement must involve a quasi-cyclic mechanism:

$$R_3\overset{\ominus}{\underset{}{Si^*}}\overset{\displaystyle O}{\cdots}\overset{}{C}Ph_2 \qquad (3\text{-}24)$$

The retention reactions of R_3Si^*OR' in nonpolar solvents are postulated to proceed by a four-center mechanism which minimizes charge separation—in accord with the low ion-solvating power of such solvents. The symbol $S_Ni\text{-}Si$ is proposed for such four-center mechanisms involving silicon as a reactive center. Figure 3-1 shows $S_Ni\text{-}Si$ transition states.

The mechanism for (3-24) is a three-center $S_Ni\text{-}Si$ process.

The $S_Ni\text{-}Si$ mechanism differs from the usual S_Ni mechanism for carbon in that the latter usually involves electron-deficient carbon in an ion-pair process (i.e., retention reactions of $ROSOCl$ to give SO_2 and RCl). Although retention of configuration for silicon by a carbon-type S_Ni process is also possible, the above four-center reactions of silicon clearly do not involve ion-pair processes (strong nucleophiles are involved), and it seems better, therefore, to label these mechanisms $S_Ni\text{-}Si$.

The probable four-center nature of the retention reactions of R_3Si^*OR' in *nonpolar solvents* (and the reality of the $S_Ni\text{-}Si$ mechanism) is greatly supported by the recent finding of inversion of configuration for each act of substitution in the neutral,

Fig. 3-1 $S_Ni\text{-}Si$ four-center reaction mechanisms:
Y is the nucleophilic and E the electrophilic part of the attacking reagent; A is a single atom or two atoms which make the quasi-cycle a five-ring or a six-ring.

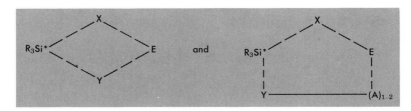

acid-catalyzed, and base-catalyzed methoxy-methoxy exchange reactions of R_3Si^*OMe in *methanol solvent.*

$$(+)R_3Si^*OMe + MeOH \longrightarrow (-)R_3Si^*OMe + MeOH$$

For an individual run, the polarimetric rate of racemization was twice the rate of detritiation observed with R_3Si^*OMe labeled with tritium in the methoxy group.[8]

The change in stereochemistry, from retention of configuration in nonpolar solvents to inversion of configuration in methanol, is easily rationalized on the basis that nonpolar solvents favor four-center retention reactions in which charge separation is minimized.

Minimization of charge separation for organosilicon reactions in general is reasonably expected to be most significant for leaving groups which, in anionic form, are very strong bases, and thus have relatively low ability to stabilize a negative charge, compared to groups such as Cl and Br. The former, which include OR', may be termed "poor leaving groups" and defined as those groups whose conjugate acids have pK_a larger than ca. 10. (Such groups generally do not undergo nucleophilic displacement from saturated carbon by bases, except in special cases such as ring-strained epoxides.) In general, such leaving groups on silicon give much slower rates than "good leaving groups" having pK_a of their conjugate acids less than ca. 6. In the absence of a polar solvent, an S_Ni-Si mechanism provides the necessary electrophilic assistance (by providing "pull" on the leaving group) and minimization of charge separation needed for removal of poor leaving groups.

In the next section it will be shown that nucleophilic reagents displace carboxylate groups, R'COO, from silicon at greatly increased rates, relative to the rates for alkoxide groups, R'O. Furthermore, displacements of R'COO proceed with inversion of configuration, even in nonpolar solvents.

Expected close similarity in the polar effects (and electronegativities) of R'O and R'COO (but not in their ability to stabilize a negative charge), and in their steric effects when R' is methyl, leads directly to the postulate that the rate-controlling transition

[8] R. Baker, R. W. Bott, C. Eaborn, *J. Organometal. Chem.,* **1,** 37 (1963).

states for nucleophilic displacements of both types of groups require considerable ionic stretching of their bonds to silicon. Only on this basis can the greatly increased rates for R'COO and the change in stereochemistry be adequately rationalized. This argument indicates that mechanism (3-25) below, which involves slow and rate-determining formation of a pentacovalent-silicon intermediate, is invalid (Y is a nucleophile, and X is R'O or R'COO).

$$R_3Si^*X + Y \underset{\text{fast}}{\overset{\text{slow}}{\rightleftharpoons}} R_3Si^* \begin{smallmatrix} X \\ \diagup \\ \diagdown \\ Y \end{smallmatrix} \xrightarrow{\text{very}}_{\text{fast}} R_3Si^*Y + X \qquad (3-25)$$

In mechanism (3-25) the rate-determining transition state would precede the expanded-octet intermediate along the reaction coordinate, and the Si—X bond would not be stretched in that transition state. Thus, the capacity of X to stabilize a negative charge could have no effect on rate or stereochemistry. We conclude that this mechanism is improbable for R_3Si^*OR' reactions.

The reaction of R_3Si^*OMe with ethylmagnesium bromide gives R_3Si^*Et of retained configuration.[9] Now, this interesting

$$(+)R_3Si^*OMe + EtMgBr \xrightarrow{90°} (+)R_3Si^*Et$$
$$[\alpha]_D +16° \qquad\qquad\qquad [\alpha]_D +3.9°$$

and significant result, which is easily rationalized on the basis of an S_Ni-Si mechanism, cannot be easily explained on the basis of a mechanism in which the ethyl anion adds to the silicon in a fast equilibrium step, followed by slow and rate-controlling breakup of the formed expanded-octet intermediate to products. There are two serious objections to such a mechanism, which can be simply stated.

Firstly, the similarity of methyl and ethyl in a full-fledged pentacovalent-silicon intermediate (four organic groups bonded to the central silicon by equally full bonds and one full bond to methoxy) would offer no significant barrier to expulsion of methyl anion from such an intermediate in the *fast* equilibrium step.

[9] L. H. Sommer, P. G. Rodewald, and G. A. Parker, *Tetrahedron Letters,* 821 (1962).

This would lead to exchange of methyl and ethyl on silicon, prior to expulsion of methoxy, by the equilibria:

$$\text{EtMgBr (excess)} + \underset{\underset{\text{Me}}{|}}{\overset{\overset{\alpha\text{-Np}}{|}}{\text{Ph}-\text{Si}-\text{OMe}}} \underset{\text{fast}}{\overset{\text{fast}}{\rightleftharpoons}}$$

$$\left[\underset{\alpha\text{-Np}}{\overset{\text{Ph}}{\diagdown}}\underset{\text{Me}}{\overset{\text{Et}}{\diagup}}\text{Si}-\text{OMe} \right]^{\ominus} \text{MgBr}^{\oplus} \underset{\text{fast}}{\overset{\text{fast}}{\rightleftharpoons}} \text{MeMgBr} + \underset{\underset{\text{Et}}{|}}{\overset{\overset{\alpha\text{-Np}}{|}}{\text{Ph}-\text{Si}-\text{OMe}}}$$

Indeed, the presence of excess ethylmagnesium bromide should promote formation of α-NpPhEtSiOMe at equilibrium, and the latter should react to give a significant amount of optically inactive α-NpPhEtSiEt. This is not observed. Indeed, the literature gives no indication that extensive substitution of one simple alkyl group by another ever obtains for the coupling reactions of organosilicon alkoxides with Grignard reagents. (Exchange of the type R′R$_2$SiOR + RMgX $\longrightarrow$ R$_3$SiOR + R′MgX is possible in the special case of special structural features in R′ which make the R′—Si bond exceptionally reactive toward nucleophiles, but this does not affect the present argument.)

Secondly, mechanism (3-26) below would reasonably be expected to lead to extensive racemization because of many acts of return to R$_3$Si*OMe prior to displacement of methoxy. Thus, on both arguments, mechanism (3-26) appears to offer too many opportunities for racemization and to be inconsistent with predominant retention of configuration.

$$\text{R}_3\text{Si}^*\text{X} + \text{Y} \underset{\text{fast}}{\overset{\text{fast}}{\rightleftharpoons}} \text{R}_3\text{Si}^*\overset{\overset{\text{X}}{\diagup}}{\underset{\underset{\text{Y}}{\diagdown}}{}} \overset{\text{slow}}{\longrightarrow} \text{R}_3\text{Si}^*\text{Y} + \text{X} \qquad (3\text{-}26)$$

On the grounds of the known stereochemistry and the arguments presented above concerning R$_3$Si*OR′, it is proposed that two major types of mechanisms obtain for reactions of R$_3$Si*OR′ with nucleophilic reagents, and probably also hold for the majority of the reactions of R_3SiOR' in general: (1) S_Ni-Si retention mechanisms in nonpolar solvents; (2) S_N2-Si mechanisms in polar solvents which generally proceed with inversion of configuration. The S_N2-Si mechanism will be discussed in detail in subsequent chapters, where it will be shown to be general for good leaving groups, even in nonpolar solvents, but we may anticipate a little and formulate an inversion S_N2-Si mechanism for R_3SiOR' (or $R_3Si\overset{\oplus}{O}HR$, etc.) as involving the following rate-controlling transition state shown in Fig. 3-2.

For an S_N2-Si transition state that has trigonal bipyramidal geometry and leads to inversion of configuration, the present author believes that a Y - - - Si - - - X arrangement in which the Y—Si—X angle is 120° (Y and X equatorial) is highly improbable. Such an arrangement would require that two of the nonreacting R groups expand their angle with the silicon from the tetrahedral value to 180°. Thus, the total amount of motion of the nonreacting R groups for attainment of such a transition state would greatly exceed that required for formation of the geometry shown in Fig. 3-2. The latter requires only a 10.5° expansion for each of the three R—Si—R angles. Furthermore, it will be pointed out later in this section that the R—Si—R angle distortion (angle contraction in this case) for S_Ni-Si reactions need be no greater than that required for attainment of the S_N2-Si transition state shown in Fig. 3-2. The present author strongly believes that *the facts of organosilicon stereochemistry compel the conclusion that minimization of motion and angle*

Fig. 3-2   Representation of a trigonal bipyramidal transition state giving inversion of configuration.

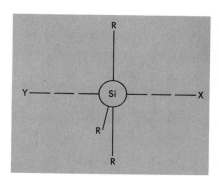

distortion for the nonreacting groups is an important factor in organosilicon mechanisms.

The above arguments against a Y - - - Si - - - X angle of 120° for inversion of configuration receive support from the observation of a retention stereochemistry for the Grignard reduction of R_3Si^*OMe. In the quasi-cyclic mechanism for this reduction (3-10) the quasi-ring is a six-ring capable of providing a 120° angle for Y - - - Si - - - X. If the latter were the preferred geometry associated with inversion of configuration, inversion of configuration should result. In fact, retention of configuration is the observed result.

As indicated in Fig. 3-2, the geometrical disposition of the three nonreacting R groups in an inversion S_N2-Si transition state is postulated to be at the equatorial positions of a trigonal bipyramid, thus resembling an S_N2 transition state for carbon (differences between S_N2-Si and S_N2 for carbon are discussed later).

In one model for an S_Ni-Si mechanism the reactant R—Si—R angles are postulated to decrease below the tetrahedral value during the process of attaining the rate-controlling transition state. This reduces nonbonded group repulsions between the R groups and X and Y. The R—Si—R angle deformation may be considered to be symmetrical (with respect to the axis defined by the Si—X bond in the reactant molecule), and not to exceed greatly the increase in R—Si—R angles which accompanies attainment of an S_N2-Si inversion transition state. The latter condition makes the amount of angle deformation and motion of the R groups approximately the same for inversion and retention reactions, ca. 10° per R—Si—R angle. In short, symmetrical deformation of the R—Si—R angles in both inversion (deformation toward X) and retention (deformation away from X) reactions results in "least motion" for the nonreacting R groups in both types of reactions. On this hypothesis, the geometrical disposition of the R groups with respect to Si in an S_Ni-Si transition state may be termed "pyramidal," and this will approximate a tetragonal pyramid arrangement (silicon out of the basal plane) when considered in relation to the positions of X and Y. (See Fig. 3-3.)

However, there is another general possibility for an S_Ni-Si transition state in which the silicon and the three R groups

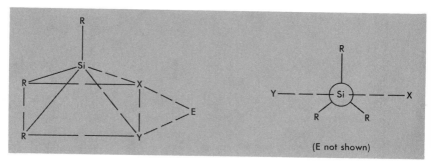

Fig. 3-3   Two views of a possible S_Ni-Si transition state having a pyramidal arrangement of the nonreacting R groups with respect to the silicon and an overall tetragonal pyramid arrangement.

are still pyramidal, but the arrangement of X and Y is such as to give an overall trigonal bipyramidal arrangement, and this is pictured in Fig. 3-4. In specific cases the actual geometry of an S_Ni-Si transition state may lie anywhere between the limits of Figs. 3-3 and 3-4.

The proposed trigonal bipyramid geometry for S_N2-Si and tetragonal pyramid or trigonal bipyramid geometry for S_Ni-Si lead directly to the possibility that stabilization of both types of transition states involves $3d$ orbital participation.   (Compare Figs. 3-2, 3-3, and 3-4 with Fig. 1-4 and its context.)   For S_N2-Si reactions, participation of the $3d_{z^2}$ orbital may be largely limited

Fig. 3-4   Two views of a possible S_Ni-Si transition state having a pyramidal arrangement of the nonreacting R groups with respect to the silicon and an overall trigonal bipyramid arrangement.

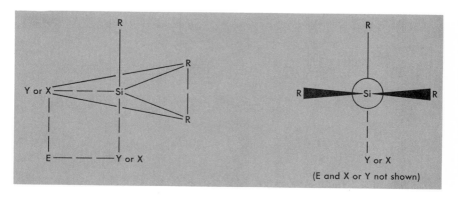

to making the long, weak "bonds" to X and Y involve two hybrid $3p_z3d_{z^2}$ orbitals of the central silicon, while the strong bonds to the three R groups largely use $3s3p^2$ hybrid orbitals of the silicon. For S_Ni-Si reactions involving tetragonal pyramid geometry, participation of the $3d_{x^2-y^2}$ orbital is indicated.

However, it must not be assumed that $3d$ orbital participation makes all five "bonds" to Si equivalent in length and strength. The heart of the models proposed is that for R_3SiOR' reactions the "bonds" to X and Y are relatively long and weak.

The above postulate of $3d$ orbital participation for stabilization of transition states raises the real possibility that the structures in Figs. 3-2, 3-3, and 3-4 may represent rate-controlling transition states *or* intermediates which are shallow valleys flanked by maxima of approximately equal heights in the free-energy profiles for the reactions of R_3SiOR'. In Fig. 3-5 curve I represents the former and curve II the latter situation.

It is interesting and important to note that the nonbonded R - - - R repulsions in the S_Ni-Si transition state represented in Fig. 3-3 are not prohibitive. For example, for an R—Si—R angle of 90° the distance between the terminal carbon atoms of the two R groups would be 2.74 Å.; for an R—Si—R angle of 100° in S_Ni-Si the carbon-carbon distance would be 2.98 Å.

Fig. 3-5   Free-energy reaction profiles for S_N2-Si and S_Ni-Si mechanisms.

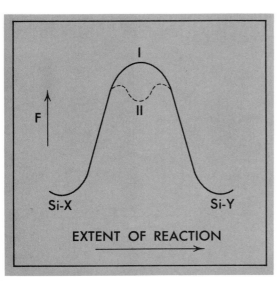

These nonbonded carbon-carbon distances are larger than the nonbonded carbon-carbon distance for two carbons which make a tetrahedral angle with a central carbon. The latter distance is 2.52 Å. From this we conclude that $3d$ orbital participation can stabilize such S_Ni-Si transition states, and the large size of silicon (covalent radius 1.17 Å. for silicon, 0.77 Å. for carbon) makes S_Ni-Si reactions possible and common.

For S_N2-Si inversion reactions the G. N. Lewis "umbrella" mechanism provides a simple and currently satisfactory model. Reagent attack at the silicon tetrahedron in this model takes place at the back face which does not contain the functional group. This mode of attack is usually termed "rearward" or "backside."

For S_Ni-Si reactions and for all retention reactions at silicon, the geometry of approach of the nucleophilic part of the attacking reagent is not so obvious and includes several possibilities which would be extremely difficult to separate on an experimental basis. For this reason the general term "frontside attack" is suggested for retention reactions at asymmetric silicon. The geometry shown in Fig. 3-3 would result from attack "broadside" to the Si—X bond. The geometry in Fig. 3-4 in which Y is apical would result from attack at one of the three front faces (which contain the functional group) of the silicon tetrahedron. The geometry in Fig. 3-4 in which Y is equatorial would result from attack at one of the three front edges (which contain the functional group) of the silicon tetrahedron. Conversion of transition states or intermediates derived from "frontside attack" to products, using the principle of "least motion," results in retention of configuration.

Before concluding this discussion of R_3SiOR' mechanisms, a nonlimiting aspect of the proposed S_Ni-Si and S_N2-Si models requires brief comment. In both mechanisms, transition-state silicon may be more negatively charged or more positively charged than reactant-state silicon, depending upon the nature of Y compared to X, and also depending upon the exact balance of bond-making and bond-breaking in the specific case being studied.

Reference to curve II in Fig. 3-5 and to the discussion of $3d$ orbital participation in σ-bonding in Chap. 1 clearly indicates that progressive replacement of R groups in R_3SiOR' by electronegative OR' groups, i.e.,

$$R_3SiOR' \longrightarrow R_2Si(OR')_2 \longrightarrow RSi(OR')_3 \longrightarrow Si(OR')_4$$

should stabilize S_Ni-Si and S_N2-Si transition states for reactions with strong nucleophiles more and more, until such stabilization culminates in the isolation of stable pentacovalent- and hexacovalent-silicon compounds in special cases; i.e. the minimum in curve II now has a lower free energy than the reactant state.

3-6   Inversion reactions of $R_3Si*OCOR$

We turn now to a discussion of the stereochemistry of $R_3Si*OCOR$ compounds in their reactions with lithium aluminum hydride, KOH(s), and methanol,[10] all in relatively nonpolar solvents. Reactions with the first two reagents allow us to discern changes in stereochemistry engendered by the change in leaving group from —OR to —OCOR, while keeping the leaving atom the same.

The reaction of $R_3Si*OCOC_6H_5$ with lithium aluminum hydride will be described in some detail as being typical of the procedure used for the reduction of four optically active acyloxysilanes. A solution of lithium aluminum hydride in ether was cooled to $-40°$ and an ether solution of the acyloxysilane was added during 15 minutes. The reaction mixture was then allowed to warm to room temperature and was stirred for an additional 20 minutes at that temperature. (Reaction is largely complete below room temperature; see below.) Decomposition of excess reducing agent with acetone followed by treatment with acid and isolation of the product gave an 83% yield of R_3Si*H.

$$(+)R_3Si*OCOC_6H_5 + LiAlH_4 \xrightarrow{-40°} (-)R_3Si*H \qquad (3\text{-}27)$$
$$[\alpha]_D +16° \qquad\qquad\qquad\qquad [\alpha]_D -24°$$

The stereospecificity was about 90% inversion of configuration. This represents a dramatic reversal of stereochemistry relative to the reduction of R_3Si*OR compounds.

---

[10] For a preliminary report on the inversion reactions of the acetoxysilane, see L. H. Sommer and C. L. Frye, *J. Am. Chem. Soc., 82,* 3796 (1960); studies on other $R_3Si*OCOR$ compounds are the work of G. A. Parker.

When the reduction of $R_3Si^*OCOC_6H_5$ was carried out at 25°, a yield of only 48% R_3Si^*H was obtained, accompanied by a 26% yield of R_3Si^*OH.

$$(+)R_3Si^*OCOC_6H_5 + LiAlH_4 \xrightarrow{25°}$$
$$[\alpha]_D +16°$$

$$(-)R_3Si^*H + (+)R_3Si^*OH \qquad (3\text{-}28)$$
$$[\alpha]_D -13° \qquad [\alpha]_D +9°$$

Consideration of (3-27) and (3-28) is interesting from several standpoints. Firstly, it is clear that the silicon atom and the carbon atom of the carbonyl group are both potential reaction sites for reduction by lithium aluminum hydride. For the benzoate, reduction at the silicon atom is favored by low temperature, presumably because this process has a lower energy of activation. The fact that reduction at the silicon atom is somewhat faster than carbonyl reduction at 25° and much faster at −40° is interesting of itself. The carbonyl group of esters is, of course, a very effective center for nucleophilic attack, but formally saturated silicon in R_3Si— compounds is apparently an even better center in lithium aluminum hydride reduction. Secondly, it is also clear that the rates of reduction at silicon in R_3Si^*OCOR compounds are much greater than those for reduction of alkoxysilanes. Faster rates and the change from predominant retention to predominant inversion of configuration are reasonably attributed to the change from a relatively poor leaving group to a good leaving group with greatly increased capacity for accepting a negative charge. This conclusion is reinforced when it is considered that one can easily write an S_Ni-Si mechanism for the lithium aluminum hydride reductions of R_3Si^*OCOR, e.g.,

$$(3\text{-}29)$$

But neither of these alternatives represents the actual mechanism.
The following stereochemical equations indicate the results

of lithium aluminum hydride reduction of three additional R_3Si^*OCOR compounds.

$$(+)R_3Si^*OCOCH_3 + LiAlH_4 \xrightarrow[-30°]{} (-)R_3Si^*H \qquad (3\text{-}30)$$
$$[\alpha]_D +18° \qquad\qquad\qquad\qquad [\alpha]_D -30°$$

$$(+)R_3Si^*OCOC_6H_4(NO_2)\text{-}p \xrightarrow[-40°]{LiAlH_4} (-)R_3Si^*H \qquad (3\text{-}31)$$
$$[\alpha]_D +22° \qquad\qquad\qquad\qquad\qquad [\alpha]_D -23°$$

$$(+)R_3Si^*OCOC_6H_3(NO_2)_2\text{-}3,5 + LiAlH_4 \xrightarrow[-70°]{}$$
$$[\alpha]_D +23°$$
$$\qquad\qquad (-)R_3Si^*H + (+)R_3Si^*OH \qquad (3\text{-}32)$$
$$\qquad\qquad [\alpha]_D -20° \qquad [\alpha]_D +7.4°$$

The yields of R_3Si^*H for (3-30), (3-31), and (3-32) were respectively 13, 76, and 61%. In (3-30) a considerable amount of *dextrorotatory* silanol was formed but was not isolated. In (3-32) a 30% yield of silanol was isolated. The lithium aluminum hydride reductions of R_3Si^*OCOR compounds all proceed with predominant inversion of configuration. The decreased optical purity of the R_3Si^*H products in (3-31) and (3-32) is probably more the result of optically impure starting materials than of decreased stereospecificity.

The reaction of $R_3Si^*OCOC_6H_5$ with KOH(s) will be described in some detail as being typical of the procedure used for three other R_3Si^*OCOR compounds. A xylene solution of the benzoxysilane was heated gently (60°) with excess powdered potassium hydroxide for a few minutes. After addition to ether, followed by washing with cold water and drying, isolation gave a 71% yield of R_3Si^*OH.

$$(+)R_3Si^*OCOC_6H_5 + KOH(s) \longrightarrow \xrightarrow{H_2O}$$
$$[\alpha]_D +18°$$
$$\qquad\qquad\qquad\qquad\qquad (-)R_3Si^*OH \qquad (3\text{-}33)$$
$$\qquad\qquad\qquad\qquad\qquad [\alpha]_D -10°$$

The silanol obtained had an optical purity of only 50%, corresponding to a stereospecificity of 75% inversion of configuration. But it is obvious that any fruitful attack of base at the carbonyl carbon would give silanol of retained configuration. The lack of optical purity may be due to carbonyl reaction or to a lack of stereospecificity, or to both. In any event, the predominant stereochemistry is inversion of configuration, and attack at the silicon center is more rapid than attack at carbonyl carbon.

The following reactions were carried out by similar procedures:

$$(+)R_3Si^*OCOCH_3 + KOH(s) \xrightarrow{} \xrightarrow{H_2O}$$
$$[\alpha]_D \ +18°$$
$$(-)R_3Si^*OH \qquad (3\text{-}34)$$
$$[\alpha]_D \ -14°$$

$$(+)R_3Si^*OCOC_6H_4(NO_2)\text{-}p + KOH(s) \xrightarrow{} \xrightarrow{H_2O}$$
$$[\alpha]_D \ +22°$$
$$(-)R_3Si^*OH \qquad (3\text{-}35)$$
$$[\alpha]_D \ -12°$$

$$(+)R_3Si^*OCOC_6H_3(NO_2)_2\text{-}3,5 + KOH(s) \xrightarrow{} \xrightarrow{H_2O}$$
$$[\alpha]_D \ +23°$$
$$(-)R_3Si^*OH \qquad (3\text{-}36)$$
$$[\alpha]_D \ -11°$$

The yields of R_3Si^*OH for (3-34), (3-35), and (3-36) were respectively 85, 95, and 95%. The predominant stereochemistry for all three reactions is inversion of configuration. Thus, the reactions of the four acyloxysilanes with $KOH(s)$ comprise a dramatic change in stereochemistry from that found for R_3Si^*OR with the same reagent in the same solvent.

As in the reduction reactions, R_3Si^*OCOR compounds give faster rates than R_3Si^*OR with $KOH(s)$. Furthermore, S_Ni-Si quasi four-ring and six-ring mechanisms can easily be written for these reactions and would lead to retention of configurations. But these cannot represent the actual mechanism. Again, the change from —OR to —OCOR, from a poor to a good leaving group better able to stabilize a negative charge, seems to demand an inversion stereochemistry.

The reaction of $R_3Si^*OCOC_6H_5$ with methanol will be described as being typical of the procedure used for the methanolysis of four R_3Si^*OCOR compounds. A solution of 1.70 g. of R_3Si^*OCOR in 20 ml. of pentane was added to a solution of 1 ml. of dry methanol and 3 ml. of cyclohexylamine in 100 ml. of pentane. A white precipitate of cyclohexylamine benzoate formed almost immediately. After 5 minutes, the amine salt was removed and the pentane solution of the product was washed with cold water and then dried. Isolation gave an 86% yield of R_3Si^*OMe.

$$(+)R_3Si^*OCOC_6H_5 + MeOH \longrightarrow (-)R_3Si^*OMe$$
$$[\alpha]_D +17° \qquad\qquad\qquad\qquad [\alpha]_D -12° \qquad (3\text{-}37)$$

By similar procedures the following results were obtained for the methanolysis of three additional R_3Si^*OCOR compounds.

$$(+)R_3Si^*OCOCH_3 + MeOH \longrightarrow (-)R_3Si^*OMe \qquad (3\text{-}38)$$
$$[\alpha]_D +16° \qquad\qquad\qquad\qquad [\alpha]_D -12°$$

$$(+)R_3Si^*OCOC_6H_4(NO_2)\text{-}p + MeOH \longrightarrow$$
$$[\alpha]_D +22°$$

$$(-)R_3Si^*OMe \qquad (3\text{-}39)$$
$$[\alpha]_D -14°$$

$$(+)R_3Si^*OCOC_6H_3(NO_2)_2\text{-}3,5 + MeOH \longrightarrow$$
$$[\alpha]_D +23°$$

$$(-)R_3Si^*OMe \qquad (3\text{-}40)$$
$$[\alpha]_D -8.6°$$

The yields of R_3Si^*OMe for (3-38), (3-39), and (3-40) were 27, 82, and 88%, respectively. Thus, for at least three of the methanolysis reactions the rate of attack at the silicon atom exceeds the rate of attack at carbonyl carbon. The latter would give silanol, R_3Si^*OH, of retained configuration.

For all four methanolysis reactions, the predominant stereochemistry is inversion of configuration. The stereospecificity varied from about 75% inversion in (3-40) to about 90% inversion in (3-39).

3-7 An inversion reaction for R_3Si^*OTs

For the development of our knowledge concerning the dynamic stereochemistry of saturated carbon, tosylates, i.e., p-toluene-sulfonates, have played an important part. The reason for this situation is that R^*OTs compounds can be prepared from optically active alcohol and p-toluenesulfonyl chloride, TsCl, without affecting the asymmetric carbon atom. Reaction of the so-prepared R*OTs compounds with diverse reagents having an entering group containing oxygen as the entering atom then reveals the stereochemistry of the R*OTs reaction automatically in a sequence such as

$$R*OH + TsCl \longrightarrow R*OTs \xrightarrow{KOH} R*OH + KOTs$$

For other reactions, such as methanolysis, all that is required is the conversion of R*OH to R*OMe via reaction of R*OK and a methyl halide; this relates the configurations of R*OH and R*OMe. In the event, a predominant inversion stereochemistry for many reactions of R*OTs has been rigorously demonstrated.

Many attempts were made to prepare and isolate $R_3Si*OTs$. All resulted in failure. Tosylate is such a good leaving group for silicon that its reaction rate with R_3Si*OH or R_3Si*OK is faster than its formation from TsCl. (A similar situation was encountered in organic chemistry when benzyl tosylate could not be formed from potassium benzylate and TsCl.) However, isolation of $R_3Si*OTs$ is not necessary for the demonstration of the stereochemistry of its reaction with R_3Si*OK. For the case of treatment of TsCl with 2 equivalents of R_3Si*OK, the following possibilities exist:

$$(-)R_3Si*OK \xrightarrow[(1)]{TsCl} R_3Si*OTs \xrightarrow[(2)]{(-)R_3Si*OK} (+)R_3Si*OSi*R_3$$
$$[\alpha]_D -70° \qquad\qquad\qquad\qquad\qquad\qquad [\alpha]_D +10°$$

$$(-)R_3Si*OK \xrightarrow[(1)]{TsCl} R_3Si*OTs \xrightarrow[(3)]{(-)R_3Si*OK} meso\text{-}R_3Si*OSi*R_3$$
$$[\alpha]_D -70° \qquad\qquad\qquad\qquad\qquad\qquad [\alpha]_D 0.0°$$

$$(-)R_3Si*OK \xrightarrow[(1)]{TsCl} R_3Si*OTs \xrightarrow[(4)]{(-)R_3Si*OK} (+)R_3Si*OSi*R_3$$
$$[\alpha]_D -70° \qquad\qquad\qquad\qquad\qquad\qquad [\alpha]_D +5°$$

If the stereochemistry of the reaction of $R_3Si*OTs$ with $(-)R_3Si*OK$ is pure retention of configuration (reaction 2), then optically pure (+)-disiloxane of $[\alpha]_D +10°$ should result. If the stereochemistry is pure inversion of configuration (reaction 3), then optically inactive meso-disiloxane should be formed. If retention and inversion have equal rates, or if $R_3Si*OTs$ racemizes completely before reaction can occur, then the product (from reaction 4) should consist of equal amounts of meso-disiloxane (optically inactive) and $(+)R_3Si^*OSi^*R_3$ having $[\alpha]_D +10°$. Thus, the net $[\alpha]_D$ should be $+5°$.

A solution containing 0.55 g. $(2.9 \times 10^{-3}$ mole$)$ of TsCl in 10 ml. of xylene was added to 20 ml. of xylene containing 5.8×10^{-3} equivalents of $(-)R_3Si^*OK$, $[\alpha]_D -70°$. Reaction at 5° was immediate. Isolation, which required chromatography over silica gel, gave a 66% yield of disiloxane as a syrup having $[\alpha]_D +1.2°$. Crystallization from pentane yielded slightly impure *meso*-disiloxane, m.p. 95.5°–97°, $[\alpha]_D +0.7°$. Optically pure, active disiloxane has m.p. 87°–89°. Based on a rotation of $[\alpha]_D +1.2°$, the stereospecificity of the reaction of R_3Si^*OK with R_3Si^*OTs is indicated to be 88% inversion of configuration.[11] Thus, the predominant stereochemistry for both —Cl and —OTs leaving groups with R_3Si^*OK in xylene is inversion of configuration. Once again, it appears that good leaving groups impose an inversion stereochemistry.

3-8   Mechanism S_N2-Si for R_3Si^*OCOR'

The generally faster rates for R_3Si^*OCOR' compared to R_3Si^*OR' compounds and the difference in stereochemistry for the two types of compounds in nonpolar solvents suggest that mechanism S_N2-Si is common for R_3Si^*OCOR' compounds, regardless of the nature of the solvent.

$$
\begin{array}{c}
R \\
| \\
Y\text{---}\!\!\overset{\displaystyle}{\underset{\overset{\displaystyle |}{\underset{\displaystyle R}{R}}}{\boxed{Si}}}\!\!\text{---}OCOR' \\
\end{array}
$$

Displacement of the tosylate group by R_3Si^*OK also takes place with inversion by mechanism S_N2-Si.

---

[11] L. H. Sommer and G. A. Parker, unpublished studies, 1962.

3-9   Summary of stereochemistry and mechanisms for R₃Si*O- compounds

For convenient reference, the stereochemical and mechanism assignments in this chapter are summarized in Table 3-1.*

Table 3-1
Summary of stereochemistry and mechanism for R₃Si*O—

R₃Si*X reactant	Reagent	Solvent	R₃Si*Y product	Stereo-chemistry	Mechanism
(+)SiOMe	t-BuMgCl	Ether	(+)SiH	Ret.	S$_N$i-Si
(+)SiO-cycloC₆H₁₁	t-BuMgCl	Ether	(−)SiH	Ret.	S$_N$i-Si
(+)SiO-t-C₄H₉	t-BuMgCl	Ether	(−)SiH	Ret.	S$_N$i-Si
(+)SiOMe	LiAlH₄	Ether	(+)SiH	Ret.	S$_N$i-Si
(−)SiO-cycloC₆H₁₁	LiAlH₄	Bu₂O	(+)SiH	Ret.	S$_N$i-Si
(−)SiO-t-C₄H₉	LiAlH₄	Bu₂O	(+)SiH	Ret.	S$_N$i-Si
(+)SiOH	LiAlH₄	Ether	(+)SiH	Ret.	S$_N$i-Si
(+)SiOSi*R₃	LiAlH₄	Bu₂O	(+)SiH	Ret.	S$_N$i-Si
(+)SiOMe	KOH (s)	Xylene	(+)SiOH^a	Ret.	S$_N$i-Si
(−)SiO-cycloC₆H₁₁	KOH (s)	Xylene	(+)SiOH^a	Ret.	S$_N$i-Si
(−)SiO-t-C₄H₉	KOH (s)	Xylene	(+)SiOH^a	Ret.	S$_N$i-Si
(+)SiOSi*R₃	KOH (s)	Xylene	(+)SiOH^a	Ret.	S$_N$i-Si
(+)SiOMe*	MeOH	MeOH	(−)SiOMe^c	Inv.	S$_N$2-Si
(+)SiOCOC₆H₅	LiAlH₄	Ether	(−)SiH	Inv.	S$_N$2-Si
(+)SiOCOCH₃	LiAlH₄	Ether	(−)SiH	Inv.	S$_N$2-Si
(+)SiOCOC₆H₄(NO₂)-p	LiAlH₄	Ether	(−)SiH	Inv.	S$_N$2-Si
(+)SiOCOC₆H₃(NO₂)₂-3,5	LiAlH₄	Ether	(−)SiH	Inv.	S$_N$2-Si
(+)SiOCOC₆H₅	KOH (s)	Xylene	(−)SiOH^a	Inv.	S$_N$2-Si
(+)SiOCOCH₃	KOH (s)	Xylene	(−)SiOH^a	Inv.	S$_N$2-Si
(+)SiOCOC₆H₄(NO₂)-p	KOH (s)	Xylene	(−)SiOH^a	Inv.	S$_N$2-Si
(+)SiOCOC₆H₃(NO₂)₂-3,5	KOH (s)	Xylene	(−)SiOH^a	Inv.	S$_N$2-Si
(+)SiOCOC₆H₅	MeOH	Pentane^b	(−)SiOMe	Inv.	S$_N$2-Si
(+)SiOCOCH₃	MeOH	Pentane^b	(−)SiOMe	Inv.	S$_N$2-Si
(+)SiOCOC₆H₄(NO₂)-p	MeOH	Pentane^b	(−)SiOMe	Inv.	S$_N$2-Si
(+)SiOCOC₆H₃(NO₂)₂-3,5	MeOH	Pentane^b	(−)SiOMe	Inv.	S$_N$2-Si
(?)SiOTs	R₃Si*OK	Xylene	meso-SiOSiR₃	Inv.	S$_N$2-Si

^{a} The actual product of these reactions is the silanolate, R₃Si*OK, which is converted to R₃Si*OH by hydrolysis.

^{b} Cyclohexylamine was used to convert the formed R'COOH to the cyclohexylammonium salt.

^{c} Reference 8.

* *Added in proof:* Detailed treatments of the syntheses and reactions in this chapter have been published recently: L. H. Sommer, C. L. Frye, and G. A. Parker, *J. Am. Chem. Soc.,* **86,** 3276 (1964); L. H. Sommer, G. A. Parker, and C. L. Frye, *ibid.,* **86,** 3281 (1964).

chapter four **Stereochemistry and mechanisms of silicon-halogen bonds**

4-1   Introduction

Perhaps the earliest mechanism postulate concerning the reactions of silicon-halogen bonds was made by Sidgwick[1] in 1927. The high reactivity of $SiCl_4$ with water, relative to the behavior of CCl_4, was attributed to the ability of silicon to expand its covalence beyond 4, thus providing a mechanism path ordinarily unavailable to saturated carbon atoms and saturated tetracovalent atoms of other first-row elements. The mechanism proposed involved addition of water to the central silicon atom, followed by splitting out of HCl.

In the years following Sidgwick's proposal, rate studies of silicon-halogen reactions, particularly those involving Si—Cl, Si—Br, and Si—I, have been few. A major difficulty, not usually encountered in rate studies of substitution reactions of saturated organic halides, is posed by the generally high reaction rates of silicon halides with certain reagents. This previously imposed the choice of certain (less reactive) Si—F compounds for study, or the alternative of special halide structures and reagents in which steric or polar factors severely decrease reactivity. It is to be hoped that the present advent of special techniques for studying very fast reactions will gradually remedy this situation in organosilicon chemistry.

In the present chapter, some significant rate studies will be discussed briefly in this section, but considerable emphasis will be placed upon recent stereochemical studies which in themselves reveal much concerning the nature of silicon-halogen reactions.

At the time of writing there appear to be three significant papers[2-4] dealing with rates of alcoholysis and hydrolysis of Ph_3SiCl and $i\text{-}Pr_3SiCl$.

In two of the papers[2,3] the nucleophilic reagent, water or methanol, was present in small concentration (ca. 2 vol. %) in nitromethane, dioxane, and isopropyl alcohol solvents. Under

[1] N. V. Sidgwick, "Electronic Theory of Valency," Oxford University Press, London, 1927, p. 157.

[2] A. D. Allen, J. C. Charlton, C. Eaborn, and G. Modena, *J. Chem. Soc.,* 3668 (1957).

[3] A. D. Allen, and G. Modena, *J. Chem. Soc.,* 3671 (1957).

[4] J. R. Chipperfield and R. H. Prince, *J. Chem. Soc.,* 3567 (1963).

these conditions rates of hydrolysis or methanolysis could be followed by a conventional titration technique. These studies showed that steric effects of substituents on rate are greatly rate-depressing. Thus, the highly hindered tri-α-naphthylchlorosilane is less reactive than Ph_3SiCl by about three powers of ten. (Although no mention was made of rates for compounds such as Me_3SiCl or Et_3SiCl, it seems safe to assume that these were found to be too reactive for study.) Concerning structural effects in the attacking reagent, the authors give the following order for reactivity: $H_2O \gg MeOH > n\text{-}PrOH > n\text{-}HexOH > i\text{-}PrOH$. It is also stated that preliminary studies at 0° indicate the following approximate reactivity relationships: i-PrOH, 1; EtOH, 10^3; MeOH, 10^4. Thus, increased steric requirements in the attacking reagent also appear to depress rate.

Although the hydrolysis of Ph_3SiCl in 1.0 M aqueous dioxane[3] at 25° could be followed by conventional techniques, and gave a first-order hydrolytic rate constant, $k_1 = 0.01$ sec.$^{-1}$, hydrolysis of Ph_3SiCl in 4.0 M aqueous acetone at 25° required the use of a rapid-reaction technique and gave $k_1 = 4.03$ sec.$^{-1}$. In the latter study, rate of hydrolysis increased rapidly with an increase in $[H_2O]$ and indicated that the rate law involves more than the first power (ca. the fourth power) of the water concentration. In the first two papers evidence was presented which showed that halide ions (or ion-pairs, etc.) caused a marked increase in rate; e.g., for reaction with 2.7×10^{-2} M water in nitromethane the first-order rate constant was increased by a factor of about 50 in the presence of 9×10^{-4} M $Et_4N^+Cl^-$. In comparison, only a small rate enhancement was produced by $Et_4N^+ClO_4^-$. In sum, the data in all three papers have been interpreted[3,4] as providing support for the following rate-controlling transition state:

$$R\text{--}\underset{\underset{\overset{|}{B}\text{---}H}{|}}{O}\text{---}\underset{R_3}{\overset{|}{Si}}\text{---}Cl$$

in which B is a base capable of assisting separation of the proton from ROH. (We shall deal with another significant fact reported in ref. 4 in a later section of this chapter.)

4-2   Inversion: a common stereochemical path
for R_3Si^*Cl and R_3Si^*Br

The hydrolysis of R_3Si^*Cl was carried out by shaking a dilute ether solution of the chloride, 0.1 mole in 500 ml. of ether, with 700 ml. of water for 1 to 2 minutes at room temperature. The ether layer was washed with water to remove acid, and dried over potassium carbonate. Removal of the solvent at reduced pressure gave a 97% yield of the product.[5]

$$(+)R_3Si^*Cl + H_2O \xrightarrow{\text{ether}} (+)R_3Si^*OH + HCl \qquad (4\text{-}1)$$
$$[\alpha]_D +6.4° \qquad\qquad\qquad [\alpha]_D +20.5°$$

A stereospecificity of at least 95% is indicated for (4-1) by subsequent conversion of R_3Si^*OH to R_3Si^*H, on the assumption that the reduction is completely stereospecific. The predominant stereochemistry for (4-1) and for the other reactions of R_3Si^*Cl discussed in this section is *inversion of configuration.* This conclusion is based on the stereochemical assignments of configuration listed in Table 2-1. These, in turn, are based on data given in Chap. 7.

Under the designated conditions of hydrolysis, it is clear that the mechanism of the reaction with water does *not* involve the path

$$R_3Si^*Cl \rightleftharpoons R_3Si^+ + Cl^-$$
$$R_3Si^+ + H_2O \rightleftharpoons R_3SiOH + H^+$$

A classical dissociated triorganosiliconium ion, which would have a plane of symmetry, cannot be involved. But, in the same connection, it is important to note that the reaction medium is ethyl ether, a relatively poor ionizing solvent of low dielectric constant.

A rather drastic change in the reagent, from water to $KOH(s)$, powdered KOH containing ca. 12% H_2O, but maintain-

---

[5] For a review and pertinent references dealing with most of the reactions discussed in Sec. 4-2, see L. H. Sommer, *Angew. Chem.,* **74,** 176 (1962); *ibid., Intern. Ed. Engl.,* **1,** 143 (1962). Many of these studies were carried out by C. L. Frye; others by G. A. Parker, P. G. Rodewald, N. C. Lloyd, and M. C. Musolf.

ing a poor ionizing solvent, still gave optically active R_3Si^*OH. The optically active chlorosilane, 1.4 g., was added to $KOH(s)$, 4 g., and 18 ml. of xylene. Shaking at room temperature gave an exothermic reaction. The chlorosilane appeared to react as fast as it dissolved. Hydrolysis of the resulting potassium salt yielded 1.2 g. of R_3Si^*OH.

$$(+)R_3Si^*Cl \xrightarrow[\text{xylene}]{KOH(s)} (-)R_3Si^*OK \xrightarrow{H_2O}$$
$$[\alpha]_D +6.1°$$

$$(+)R_3Si^*OH \qquad (4\text{-}2)$$
$$[\alpha]_D +16.0°$$

The stereospecificity for the conversion of chloride to R_3Si^*OK is probably at least 90%. Although the conversion of the salt to silanol need not affect the asymmetric center, R_3Si^*OH is racemized by aqueous alkali, which is formed during the hydrolysis, at a fair rate.

The methanolysis of R_3Si^*Cl was carried out by rapid addition of a dilute solution in pentane, 14 g. of chloride and 150 ml. of solvent, to a solution composed of 10 ml. of methanol, 20 ml. of cyclohexylamine as an HCl acceptor, and 300 ml. of pentane. After shaking for 1 to 2 minutes at room temperature, the reaction mixture was washed with water to remove excess amine and formed amine hydrochloride. Removal of the solvent under reduced pressure gave the product in 90% yield.

$$(+)R_3Si^*Cl + MeOH \xrightarrow[\text{pentane}]{C_6H_{11}NH_2} (+)R_3Si^*OMe \qquad (4\text{-}3)$$
$$[\alpha]_D +6.1° \qquad\qquad\qquad\qquad [\alpha]_D +17.0°$$

The methanolysis proceeds with inversion of configuration to the extent of at least 90%, as indicated by subsequent reduction of R_3Si^*OMe and assuming the reduction to be completely stereospecific.

By a procedure similar to that used for methanolysis, except that a longer reaction time of 25 minutes was used because of the slower rate, the reaction with cyclohexanol gave a 30% yield of the cyclohexoxysilane after fractional distillation.

$$(+)R_3Si^*Cl + cycloC_6H_{11}OH \xrightarrow[\text{pentane}]{C_6H_{11}NH_2}$$
$$[\alpha]_D +6.2°$$

$$(-)R_3Si^*O\text{-}cycloC_6H_{11} \qquad (4\text{-}4)$$
$$[\alpha]_D -8.0°$$

The by-products, R_3Si^*OH and $R_3Si^*OSi^*R_3$, resulted from hydrolysis and condensation which may have occurred during treatment with water after the cyclohexanolysis was presumed to be complete. The stereospecificity of (4-4) is again at least 90%, as indicated by subsequent reduction of R_3Si^*O-cycloC_6H_{11} to R_3Si^*H with $LiAlH_4$ and the assumption of complete stereospecificity for the reduction.

By a procedure similar to that used for the reaction with cyclohexanol, R_3Si^*Cl was treated with $(-)$menthol. The yield of diastereomeric menthoxysilane was only 14% owing to the difficulty of separating the product from excess $(-)$menthol. But the reaction was highly stereospecific and proceeded with at least 95% inversion of configuration. (The starting chlorosilane was only 82% optically pure.)

$$(-)R_3Si^*Cl + (-)MenOH \xrightarrow[\text{pentane}]{\text{cycloC}_6\text{H}_{11}\text{NH}_2}$$
$$[\alpha]_D -5.1°$$
$$(+)R_3Si^*—(-)OMen \quad (4\text{-}5)$$
$$[\alpha]_D -37°$$

Reduction of the $(-)R_3Si^*OMen$ obtained from the $(-)$chlorosilane gave R_3Si^*H having $[\alpha]_D -28°$.

Reaction of the optically active chlorosilane with potassium t-butoxide in dilute t-butyl alcohol solution gave a 62% yield of optically active product after heating at 70° for 2 to 3 minutes.

$$(+)R_3Si^*Cl + KO\text{-}t\text{-}C_4H_9 \xrightarrow{t\text{-}C_4H_9OH} (-)R_3Si^*O\text{-}t\text{-}C_4H_9$$
$$[\alpha]_D +6.2° \qquad\qquad\qquad [\alpha]_D -28.1° \quad (4\text{-}6)$$

A stereospecificity of at least 90% is indicated for (4-6) by subsequent conversion of the product to R_3Si^*H, on the assumption that the reduction is completely stereospecific.

The optically active methoxysilane was also prepared in high optical purity by treatment of a dilute ether solution of R_3Si^*Cl with $NaB(OMe)_4$ at room temperature for 10 minutes. Treatment with water after addition of pentane to precipitate most of the boron compounds, followed by drying and removal of solvent, gave a 95% yield of product.

$$(+)R_3Si^*Cl + NaB(OMe)_4 \xrightarrow{\text{ether}} (+)R_3Si^*OMe \quad (4\text{-}7)$$
$$[\alpha]_D +6.1° \qquad\qquad\qquad\qquad [\alpha]_D +17.0°$$

By a similar procedure the reaction with $NaBH(OMe)_3$ in ether solvent yielded the methoxysilane contaminated with a very small amount of R_3Si^*H. The yield was 99%.

$$(+)R_3Si^*Cl + NaBH(OMe)_3 \xrightarrow{\text{ether}} (+)R_3Si^*OMe \qquad (4\text{-}8)$$
$$[\alpha]_D +6.1° \qquad\qquad\qquad [\alpha]_D +14.5°$$

Treatment of a dilute benzene solution of R_3Si^*Cl with excess powdered potassium acetate at room temperature for 23 hours gave

$$(+)R_3Si^*Cl + KOAc \xrightarrow{\text{benzene}} (+)R_3Si^*OAc \qquad (4\text{-}9)$$
$$[\alpha]_D +5.88° \qquad\qquad [\alpha]_D +15.2°$$

Reaction (4-9) is highly stereospecific, at least 90% inversion, as indicated by the conversion of R_3Si^*OAc to R_3Si^*H, the assumption of complete stereospecificity for the reduction, and consideration of the fact that the starting R_3Si^*Cl had an optical purity of only about 90%. Optically pure R_3Si^*OAc has $[\alpha]_D +17.7°$.

The change from potassium acetate to the more electrophilic mercuric acetate still gave inversion of configuration as the predominant stereochemical path. A dilute benzene solution of R_3Si^*Cl was heated with excess mercuric acetate at 80° for 2 hours and gave a 92% yield of product.

$$(+)R_3Si^*Cl + Hg(OAc)_2 \xrightarrow{\text{benzene}} (+)R_3Si^*OAc \qquad (4\text{-}10)$$
$$[\alpha]_D +5.8° \qquad\qquad\qquad [\alpha]_D +13°$$

The observed stereospecificity is lower for (4-10) than for (4-9), but the racemization rate of R_3Si^*OAc with $Hg(OAc)_2$ may be competitive with the displacement.

Reaction of a dilute solution of R_3Si^*Cl in chloroform with cyclohexylamine acetate is complete in minutes. Use of equimolar amounts of the reactants gave a 95% yield of product.

$$(+)R_3Si^*Cl + cycloC_6H_{11}NH_3OAc \xrightarrow{\text{CHCl}_3}$$
$$[\alpha]_D +5.4°$$
$$(+)R_3Si^*OAc + C_6H_{11}NH_3Cl \qquad (4\text{-}11)$$
$$[\alpha]_D +13°$$

The change from cyclohexylamine acetate to the benzoate salt gave the benzoate, R_3Si^*OBz, in 80% yield with a stereospecificity of at least 90% inversion.

$$(+)R_3Si^*Cl + cycloC_6H_{11}NH_3OBz \xrightarrow{CHCl_3}$$
$$[\alpha]_D +5.4°$$
$$(+)R_3Si^*OBz + C_6H_{11}NH_3Cl \quad (4\text{-}12)$$
$$[\alpha]_D +18.5°$$

The reaction of optically active R_3Si^*OK in xylene solution with R_3Si^*Cl proceeds very rapidly at room temperature with evolution of heat.

$$(+)R_3Si^*Cl + (-)R_3Si^*OK \xrightarrow{xylene}$$
$$[\alpha]_D +6.1° \quad [\alpha]_D -75°$$
$$(+)R_3Si^*OSi^*R_3 + KCl \quad (4\text{-}13)$$
$$[\alpha]_D +9.8°$$

$$(-)R_3Si^*Cl + (-)R_3Si^*OK \xrightarrow{xylene}$$
$$[\alpha]_D -6.1° \quad [\alpha]_D -75°$$
$$meso\text{-}R_3Si^*OSi^*R_3 + KCl \quad (4\text{-}14)$$
$$[\alpha]_D +0.45°$$

Reaction (4-13) is at least 90% stereospecific. The small rotation observed for the meso product indicates that the starting materials were not completely optically pure or that the reaction is not 100% stereospecific.

We may summarize the general significance of the stereochemical equations (4-1) to (4-14) by the following statement:

For the general change $R_3Si^*Cl \longrightarrow R_3Si^*O$—, the use of diverse reagents and poor ionizing solvents gives rapid reactions (in homogeneous cases) which proceed with predominant inversion of configuration.

From the standpoint of involvement of $d_\pi\text{-}p_\pi$ bonding in the rate-determining transition states of these reactions, both the entering and leaving groups can participate in such bonding because both have filled nonbonding p orbitals.

We turn now to a discussion of some reduction reactions of R_3Si^*Cl. A solution of optically active chlorosilane in pentane, 1.78 g. of chloride in 20 ml. of solvent, was added to a solution of

1 g. of lithium aluminum hydride in 100 ml. of dry ether. *The reduction was immediate* and exothermal. After swirling of the reactants for one minute, the solution was poured into a mixture of hydrochloric acid and ether. After separation of the organic layer, washing, drying, and removal of solvent at reduced pressure, there was obtained a 96% yield of product.

$$(+)R_3Si^*Cl + LiAlH_4 \xrightarrow{\text{ether}} (+)R_3Si^*H \qquad (4\text{-}15)$$
$$[\alpha]_D +6.3° \qquad\qquad\qquad [\alpha]_D +35°$$

The stereospecificity of this reaction is at least 95% as shown by reconversion of R_3Si^*H to R_3Si^*Cl.

Reduction of R_3Si^*Cl with sodium borohydride in diglyme solvent gave optically active R_3Si^*H of considerably lower optical purity.

$$(+)R_3Si^*Cl + NaBH_4 \xrightarrow{\text{diglyme}} (+)R_3Si^*H \qquad (4\text{-}16)$$
$$[\alpha]_D +5.8° \qquad\qquad\qquad [\alpha]_D +15°$$

It is probable that the observed lack of optical purity of the product in this case is due to racemization of R_3Si^*Cl by sodium chloride, which has some solubility in diglyme. Optically active R_3Si^*H is not racemized by sodium borohydride in diglyme after 30 minutes at steam-bath temperature.

From the standpoint of involvement of $d_\pi\text{-}p_\pi$ bonding in the rate-determining transition states of (4-15) and (4-16), it is interesting to note that these reactions cannot involve the entering group in such bonding. Nevertheless, for these cases of greatly decreased $d_\pi\text{-}p_\pi$ bonding between the entering group and the silicon atom, inversion is still the predominant stereochemical path.

Reactions of optically active bromosilane, R_3Si^*Br, were carried out by procedures similar to those used for R_3Si^*Cl in (4-1), (4-2), (4-6), (4-8), (4-13), and (4-15). In every case which was studied, the predominant stereochemistry was inversion of configuration. Stereospecificity was generally somewhat less, in the range 80 to 90%, but this is likely due to the greater rates of racemization for R_3Si^*Br.

4-3   Solvent-induced racemization of R_3Si^*Cl: evidence for an ionization mechanism

Subsequent to the demonstration of predominant inversion as the stereochemical path for reactions of R_3Si^*Cl with diverse reagents in poor ionizing solvents, an investigation of the racemization of this compound was begun. The data obtained thus far have some interesting features.[6]

When R_3Si^*Cl, $[\alpha]_D$ $-6.3°$ in pentane, is dissolved in carefully purified solvents, the solutions can be divided into two broad categories: those which exhibit optical activity and those which are initially optically inactive. This effect is illustrated by the data of Table 4-1 for solvents demonstrated not to react with the chlorosilane by a displacement reaction, i.e., those solvents from which optically active or inactive chlorosilane could be recovered or shown to be present by an infrared spectrum. It should be noted that the optically active solutions show no decrease in rotation after 24 hours, whereas the inactive solutions exhibit no rotation immediately after the dissolution of the chlorosilane. Furthermore, the zero rotation of the inactive solutions was shown not to be merely a solvent effect on the extent of rotation of optically active R_3Si^*Cl; isolation of the solid chlorosilane by solvent removal under vacuum followed by dissolution in pentane gave optically inactive solutions.

The data in Table 4-1 have some interesting aspects. Firstly, it may be noted that solvents of low dielectric constant but rela-

[6] L. H. Sommer and F. O. Stark, unpublished work; see F. O. Stark, Ph.D. Thesis, The Pennsylvania State University, 1962.

Table 4-1
Observed optical rotations for solutions of R_3Si^*Cl

Solvent	Observed rotation[a]	Solvent	Observed rotation[a]
Chloroform	$-1.32°$	Carbon tetrachloride	$-1.32°$
Benzene	$-1.33°$	Dioxane	$-1.58°$
Chlorobenzene	$-1.33°$	Acetonitrile	$0.00°$
Tetrahydrofuran	$-1.62°$	Nitromethane	$0.00°$
Pentane	$-1.32°$	Nitrobenzene	$0.00°$

[a] Rotations measured on 1.0 g. of R_3Si^*Cl in 12 ml. of solution using a 2.5-decimeter tube.

Table 4-2

Rate constants for the racemizations of $(-)$-α-NpPhMeSiCl (0.189 M) at 25.0°C. in anhydrous nitromethane-chloroform solvents of various composition

% nitromethane	$k_{1(rac.)}$ min.$^{-1}$	% nitromethane	$k_{1(rac.)}$ min.$^{-1}$
15	2.2×10^{-4}	70	4.2×10^{-1}
20	2.8×10^{-3}	75	4.6×10^{-1}
25	6.2×10^{-3}	80	6.9×10^{-1}
30	1.6×10^{-2}	85	7.6×10^{-1}
35	3.4×10^{-2}	90	1.1
40	6.6×10^{-2}	85	7.8×10^{-1}
45	1.0×10^{-1}	65	3.5×10^{-1}
50	1.6×10^{-1}	50	1.8×10^{-1}
55	2.0×10^{-1}	30	1.6×10^{-2}
60	2.5×10^{-1}	20	2.5×10^{-3}
65	3.8×10^{-1}		

tively high basicity, tetrahydrofuran and dioxane, do not give any racemization during 24 hours. Secondly, it seems clear that solvents of high dielectric constant and relatively low basicity, nitromethane and nitrobenzene, give extremely rapid racemization. All the data in Table 4-1 are in accord with a solvent-induced racemization whose rate depends critically on the dielectric constant of the solvent. Excellent support for this conclusion is based on studies of the racemization of R_3Si^*Cl induced by mixed solvents. Carefully purified dry solvents (all transfers in a dry box under nitrogen) were used to study the rates of racemization of R_3Si^*Cl in nitromethane-chloroform solvents. Excellent first-order rate plots were obtained and yielded the rate constants listed in Table 4-2.

Figure 4-1 illustrates the profound effect of dielectric constant on $k_{1(rac.)}$ and supports an ionization hypothesis. The data in Table 4-2 show that *a sixfold increase in nitromethane concentration produces an increase in $k_{1(rac.)}$ of more than three powers of ten.*

There is no significant change in the rate of racemization when large amounts of anhydrous HCl are added, up to 10% of the concentration of the chlorosilane. Furthermore, there is no

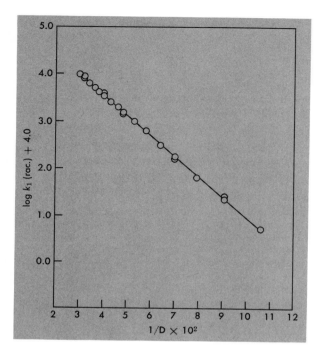

Fig. 4-1 Plot of $\log k_{1(\text{rac.})}$ versus $1/D$ for solvent-induced racemization of α-NpPhMeSiCl.

significant change in $k_{1(\text{rac.})}$ with change in the concentration of R_3Si^*Cl. These facts effectively dispose of alternatives to solvent-induced racemization.

A racemization mechanism involving addition of a nitromethane molecule to R_3Si^*Cl to give an expanded-octet intermediate which returns to R_3Si^*Cl with inversion of configuration may also be eliminated. In pure nitromethane, R_3Si^*F is only 6% racemized after 120 hours. The latter should be racemized more rapidly than R_3Si^*Cl if such a mechanism were operating. (See Sec. 4-5.)

Before concluding this section it seems appropriate to point out that conductance studies (Sec. 1-7), which indicate a low equilibrium concentration of dissociated siliconium ions in solutions of R_3SiCl compounds in various solvents, are in no way inconsistent with siliconium ion-pairs as reaction intermediates. (Indeed, conductance studies do not even obviate the possibility of dissociated, solvated siliconium ions as reaction intermediates because of the often-observed lack of parallelism between rate and equilibrium.)

The exact nature of the ionic intermediate in the solvent-induced racemization is, of course, not known. There are two broad alternatives: (1) an intimate ion-pair which is externally solvated; (2) a solvent-separated or external ion-pair. In either event, racemization proceeds via ion-pair return.[7] S is solvent in the following equations:

$$(+)R_3Si^*Cl \rightleftharpoons [R_3Si^*]^{\oplus}\cdots[Cl]^{\ominus} \rightleftharpoons (-)R_3Si^*Cl$$
$$(+)R_3Si^*Cl \rightleftharpoons [R_3Si^*]^{\oplus}\cdots S\cdots[Cl]^{\ominus} \rightleftharpoons (-)R_3Si^*Cl$$

Racemization of R_3Si^*Cl by ion-pair return would involve rotation of one component of the ion-pair with respect to the other or sliding of one component past the other. S. Winstein and coworkers and other investigators have clearly shown this type of behavior for carbonium ion-pairs.[7]

For racemization of R_3Si^*Cl by external ion-pair return, there is, at present, no rigorous way of deciding whether nitromethane simply "solvates" the siliconium ion or whether some coordination to silicon is involved. The linear relationship in Fig. 4-1, however, suggests that simple "solvation" is involved.

4-4 Inversion and retention reactions of R_3Si^*F

Reduction of R_3Si^*F with lithium aluminum hydride in dilute ether solution gave a 99% yield of R_3Si^*H after one hour at reflux temperature.

$$(+)R_3Si^*F + LiAlH_4 \xrightarrow{\text{ether}} (-)R_3Si^*H \qquad (4\text{-}17)$$
$$[\alpha]_D +46° \qquad\qquad\qquad [\alpha]_D -32°$$

The stereospecificity was at least 95%. The stereochemical course was predominant inversion.

---

[7] For precise explanation of the terms "intimate ion-pair," "external ion-pair," and "ion-pair return," see S. Winstein, E. Clippinger, A. H. Fainberg, R. Heck, and G. C. Robinson, *J. Am. Chem. Soc.*, **78**, 328 (1956).

The reaction of a dilute solution of R_3Si^*F in xylene with optically active R_3Si^*OK in the same solvent was complete in one minute at room temperature.

$$(+)R_3Si^*F + (-)R_3Si^*OK \xrightarrow{\text{xylene}}$$
$$[\alpha]_D +42° \qquad [\alpha]_D -75°$$
$$(+)R_3Si^*OSi^*R_3 + KF \qquad (4\text{-}18)$$
$$[\alpha]_D +8.1°$$

The stereospecificity was at least 90%, and the predominant stereochemistry was *retention of configuration,* as indicated by Table 2-1 which assigns the same configuration to $(+)R_3Si^*F$ and $(-)R_3Si^*Cl$. Thus, for reaction with R_3Si^*OK in xylene the change from R_3Si^*Cl [Eqs. (4-13) and (4-14)] to R_3Si^*F changes the predominant stereochemistry from inversion to retention.

4-5   Racemization of R_3Si^*F without displacement of fluoride ion: expanded-octet (EO) return

The optically active fluorosilane R_3Si^*F does not undergo racemization when dissolved in dry pentane or *t*-butyl alcohol. However, in both solvents racemization is caused by added methanol.

Polarimetric rate data for racemization of R_3Si^*F (0.0358 M) in pentane by methanol (0.580 M) at 31.2° gave a linear first-order plot, $k_1 = 3.5 \times 10^{-2}$ min.$^{-1}$. When racemization of an equimolar mixture of R_3Si^*F and optically active R_3Si^*OMe (0.0179 M) in each component was carried out, the optical rotation only decreased to the expected value for the optically active methoxysilane and remained constant at that value for 26 hours. Thus, the racemization of the fluorosilane does not involve the methoxysilane as an intermediate. Furthermore, the product of the racemization is pure, racemic fluorosilane. Therefore, the fluorosilane is racemized without macroscopic or microscopic replacement of fluoride ion.

In the presence of HF (7.5×10^{-4} M), and keeping the methanol and fluorosilane concentrations constant, the rate constant for racemization decreased from 3.5×10^{-2} to 4.0×10^{-5} min.$^{-1}$, by a factor of almost 10^3. In pentane solvent, racemization rate increases rapidly with increasing methanol concentration. Indeed, the order of reaction with respect to methanol was found to be approximately 4. In an extremely nonpolar solvent such as pentane, this does not mean that four molecules of methanol are covalently bonded to R_3Si^*F in the rate-controlling transition state.

The rate data for racemization of R_3Si^*F (0.0358 M) in t-butyl alcohol by methanol (2.06 M) at 25° give a linear first-order plot, $k_1 = 2.0$ min.$^{-1}$. In t-butyl alcohol solvent, as in pentane, an equimolar mixture of R_3Si^*F and R_3Si^*OMe was racemized by methanol only to the point of complete racemization of R_3Si^*F and zero racemization of R_3Si^*OMe. Both HF (8.44×10^{-2} M) and boron trifluoride etherate (0.529 M) retard racemization of R_3Si^*F by methanol in the t-butyl alcohol solvent, the former by a factor of 17 and the latter by a factor of 4, for $[R_3Si^*F]$ equal to 0.0358 M and $[CH_3OH]$ equal to 0.580 M.

The experimental data and conclusions which follow directly from them amount to the following:

1. Optically active R_3Si^*F in pentane and t-butyl alcohol solvents is racemized by added methanol without displacement of —F.

2. Such racemization cannot be due to fluoride-fluoride exchange engendered by formation of a small amount of HF. Addition of HF to the reaction medium strongly retards the rate of racemization.

3. Such racemization cannot be due to the formation of ionic intermediates containing ionized fluorine. The high bond energy of Si—F and the low dielectric constants of the t-butyl alcohol and pentane solvents argue against such a possibility. Furthermore, in pure formic acid, a solvent of high ionizing power, the pseudo first-order rate constant for racemization of R_3Si^*F is only 3.7×10^{-3} min.$^{-1}$, compared to 3.5×10^{-2} min.$^{-1}$ in pentane containing 0.580 M methanol. Also, ionic intermediates containing ionic fluorine should be considerably stabilized by the presence of HF, due to probable formation of HF_2^- from such intermediates. Instead, rate retardation is observed when HF is added. In addition, we have already noted (Sec. 4-3) that the high-dielectric-constant solvent nitromethane which ionizes R_3Si^*Cl gives racemization of R_3Si^*F at very slow rates.

On the basis of the above data it seems safe to conclude that

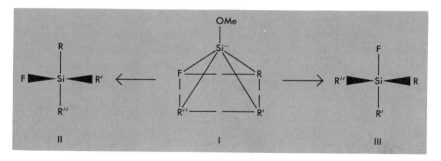

Fig. 4-2   Expanded-octet return, EO return, for R_3Si^*F.

the racemization of R_3Si^*F by methanol in pentane and t-butyl alcohol solvents proceeds by a mechanism which involves equilibrium formation of an expanded-octet silicon intermediate. Addition of methoxide ion (from $MeOH_2^+—MeO^-$) to the central silicon to give a geometrical arrangement in which R, R', R'', and F are coplanar constitutes a possible mechanism for the racemization.   For a pentacovalent-silicon intermediate, the organic groups and the fluorine would be *basal* in a tetragonal pyramid, and methoxide would be *apical*.   Such an intermediate (I) would be optically active and could return to R_3Si^*F with *retention* or *inversion* of configuration, depending upon which pair of trans groups (R and R'' or R' and F) move toward the methoxy group as it leaves.   This situation is represented in Fig. 4-2, which also proposes the term "expanded-octet return," EO return, for this type of racemization of R_3Si^*X.

Structure III, resulting from movement of R and R'' toward MeO^-, is the enantiomer of structure II which results from movement of R' and F toward MeO^-.

Structure I may, of course, also derive from reaction of R_3Si^*F with two molecules of methanol as an alternative to reaction with $MeOH_2^+—MeO^-$.   In either case, addition of HF should decrease rate by decreasing the basicity of the medium. This effect should be, and is, more pronounced in pentane than in t-butyl alcohol.

Structure I must exist as one component of an ion-pair which also contains $MeOH_2^+$.   One or more molecules of methanol stabilize the ion-pair by solvation.

It is important that the phenomenon of EO return for R_3Si^*F be placed in proper perspective with regard to the reactions of R_3SiX in general. Like solvent-induced racemization of R_3Si^*Cl by ion-pair return, *solvent-induced racemization of R_3Si^*F by EO return represents deviation from the usual behavior of R_3Si^*X in its many stereospecific reactions.* If EO return were generally faster than S_N2-Si and S_Ni-Si displacement reactions, then stereospecific reactions of R_3Si^*X would be unknown. The same is true of ion-pair return. We may conclude that EO return is uncommon for R_3Si^*X reactions in general.

The high bond energy of Si—F (ca. 130 kcal./mole), the high electronegativity of fluorine, 4.0 on the Pauling scale, and the small size of covalently bonded fluorine, covalent radius 0.72 Å, all suggest that EO return is especially favored for R_3Si^*F.

$$(+)R_3Si^*F + Y \rightleftharpoons R_3Si^*FY \rightleftharpoons (-)R_3SiF + Y$$

But even R_3Si^*F undergoes stereospecific reactions with nucleophiles. This indicates, again, that EO return is generally not the path of lowest $\Delta F\ddagger$ for R_3SiX reactions.[8]

4-6 Mechanisms of R_3Si^*Hal compounds: discussion of S_N2-Si, S_N1-Si, S_N2^*-Si, and S_Ni-Si mechanisms

All the inversion reactions discussed above for R_3Si^*Cl and R_3Si^*Br involve entering groups which are stronger bases than —Cl or —Br. For such reactions of R_3Si^*Cl and R_3Si^*Br an S_N2-Si mechanism seems especially probable. This conclusion is supported by the fact that the reaction of R_3Si^*Cl with ethyllithium gives predominant inversion of configuration:[9]

$$(-)R_3Si^*Cl + EtLi \xrightarrow{\text{ether}} (-)R_3Si^*Et$$

By the arguments already presented in Sec. 3-5 this eliminates a fast equilibrium formation of a pentacovalent-silicon intermediate followed by slow breakup to products. The other alternative, slow formation of a pentacovalent-silicon intermediate followed by fast breakup to products, is made improbable for hydrolysis of

---

[8] L. H. Sommer and P. G. Rodewald, *J. Am. Chem. Soc.*, **85**, 3898 (1963).

[9] L. H. Sommer, P. G. Rodewald, and G. A. Parker, *Tetrahedron Letters*, 821 (1962).

R_3SiCl by some recent work on the hydrolysis of triisopropyl-chlorosilane in acetone-water using fast-reaction techniques.[4] The first-order rate constant for this hydrolysis obtained within 4.5 millisec. to 0.6 sec. was the same as that obtained over 20 sec. If an intermediate were involved, the rate constant should increase during the time required to reach its steady-state concentration.[4] Thus, for the many inversion reactions of R_3Si^*Cl and R_3Si^*Br with strong nucleophiles, the most probable structure of the rate-controlling transition state is

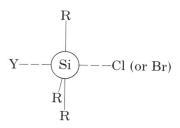

It is proposed that ionization mechanisms, regardless of whether they involve a classical dissociated triorganosiliconium ion, a siliconium ion-pair, or a siliconium ion chelated with one or more molecules of nonreacting solvent, be termed S_N1-Si. By this definition, the solvent-induced racemization of R_3Si^*Cl is an example of an S_N1-Si mechanism.

It is proposed that mechanisms involving fast equilibrium formation of an expanded-octet silicon intermediate in which none of the original four bonds to silicon are significantly stretched be termed an S_N2^*-Si mechanism. By this definition, the methanol-induced racemization of R_3Si^*F described above is an example of an S_N2^*-Si mechanism operating to give EO return in this specific case.

The retention reaction of R_3Si^*F with R_3Si^*OK in xylene is likely an example of an S_Ni-Si mechanism, as is also the retention reaction of R_3Si^*F with ethyllithium in ether.[9]

$$(+)R_3Si^*F + EtLi \xrightarrow{\text{ether}} (+)R_3Si^*Et$$

The factors contributing to operation of EO return and an S_N2^*-Si mechanism for R_3Si^*F have been summarized in the preceding section. The same factors, plus the ability of $-F$ to give ready coordination with electrophilic centers, contribute to operation of mechanism S_Ni-Si for R_3Si^*F.

The inversion reactions of R_3Si^*F probably proceed by mechanism S_N2-Si. Thus, *three* mechanisms probably obtain in the special case of R_3SiF compounds: S_Ni-Si, S_N2-Si, and S_N2^*-Si, including EO return with racemization and without displacement of $-F$.

4-7   Summary of stereochemistry and mechanisms for R_3Si^*Hal compounds

For convenient reference, the stereochemical and mechanism assignments in this chapter are summarized in Table 4-3.

Table 4-3
Summary of stereochemistry and mechanism for R_3Si^*Hal compounds

R_3Si^*X reactant	Reagent	Solvent	R_3Si^*Y product	Stereo-chemistry	Mechanism
$(+)SiCl$	H_2O	Ether	$(+)SiOH$	Inv.	S_N2-Si
$(+)SiCl$	$KOH(s)$	Xylene	$(-)SiOK$	Inv.	S_N2-Si
$(+)SiCl$	$MeOH^a$	Pentane	$(+)SiOMe$	Inv.	S_N2-Si
$(+)SiCl$	$cycloC_6H_{11}OH^a$	Pentane	$(-)SiO\text{-}cycloC_6H_{11}$	Inv.	S_N2-Si
$(-)SiCl$	$(-)MenOH^a$	Pentane	$(+)Si\text{-}(-)OMen$	Inv.	S_N2-Si
$(+)SiCl$	$KO\text{-}t\text{-}C_4H_9$	$t\text{-}C_4H_9OH$	$(-)SiO\text{-}t\text{-}C_4H_9$	Inv.	S_N2-Si
$(+)SiCl$	$NaB(OMe)_4$	Ether	$(+)SiOMe$	Inv.	S_N2-Si
$(+)SiCl$	$NaBH(OMe)_3$	Ether	$(+)SiOMe$	Inv.	S_N2-Si
$(+)SiCl$	CH_3CO_2K	C_6H_6	$(+)SiOCOMe$	Inv.	S_N2-Si
$(+)SiCl$	$Hg(OCOMe)_2$	C_6H_6	$(+)SiOCOMe$	Inv.	S_N2-Si
$(+)SiCl$	$cycloC_6H_{11}NH_3OCOMe$	$CHCl_3$	$(+)SiOCOMe$	Inv.	S_N2-Si
$(+)SiCl$	$cycloC_6H_{11}NH_3OCOPh$	$CHCl_3$	$(+)SiOCOC_6H_5$	Inv.	S_N2-Si
$(+)SiCl$	$(-)R_3Si^*OK$	Xylene	$(+)SiOSi^*R_3$	Inv.	S_N2-Si
$(-)SiCl$	$(-)R_3Si^*OK$	Xylene	$meso\text{-}SiOSiR_3$	Inv.	S_N2-Si

^{a} Cyclohexylamine was used as an acceptor for formed acid.

Table 4-3 (cont.)
Summary of stereochemistry and mechanism for R_3Si^*Hal compounds

R_3Si^*X reactant	Reagent	Solvent	R_3Si^*Y product	Stereo-chemistry	Mechanism
$(+)$SiCl	$LiAlH_4$	Ether	$(+)$SiH	Inv.	S_N2-Si
$(+)$SiCl	$NaBH_4$	Diglyme	$(+)$SiH	Inv.	S_N2-Si
$(+)$SiBr	H_2O	Ether	$(+)$SiOH	Inv.	S_N2-Si
$(+)$SiBr	KOH(s)	Xylene	$(-)$SiOK	Inv.	S_N2-Si
$(+)$SiBr	KO-t-C_4H_9	t-C_4H_9OH	$(-)$SiO-t-C_4H_9	Inv.	S_N2-Si
$(+)$SiBr	$NaBH(OMe)_3$	Ether	$(+)$SiOMe	Inv.	S_N2-Si
$(+)$SiBr	$(-)R_3Si^*OK$	Xylene	$(+)SiOSi^*R_3$	Inv.	S_N2-Si
$(+)$SiBr	$LiAlH_4$	Ether	$(+)$SiH	Inv.	S_N2-Si
$(+)$SiCl		CH_3NO_2	$(\pm)$SiCl	Rac.	S_N1-Si[b]
$(+)$SiF	$LiAlH_4$	Ether	$(-)$SiH	Inv.	S_N2-Si
$(+)$SiF	$(-)R_3Si^*OK$	Xylene	$(+)SiOSi^*R_3$	Ret.	S_Ni-Si
$(+)$SiF	EtLi	Ether	$(+)$SiEt	Ret.	S_Ni-Si
$(-)$SiCl	EtLi	Ether	$(-)$SiEt	Inv.	S_N2-Si
$(+)$SiF	MeOH	t-C_4H_9OH	$(\pm)$SiF	Rac.	S_N2^*-Si[c]

[b] Ion-pair return.
[c] Expanded-octet (EO) return.

chapter
five # Halide-halide exchange at asymmetric silicon: S_N2-Si and S_N1-Si mechanisms

5-1   Introduction

In the previous chapter (Sec. 4-2), the reactions of R_3Si^*Cl with cyclohexylamine salts of carboxylic acids, in chloroform solvent, were shown to proceed with inversion of configuration by an S_N2-Si mechanism.   But the solvent-induced racemization of R_3Si^*Cl in nitromethane-chloroform solvents by an S_N1-Si mechanism raised the possibility that other cases of an S_N1-Si mechanism might be isolated if the basicity (and nucleophilicity) of the attacking nucleophile were low enough to permit mechanism S_N1-Si to predominate.   For this and other reasons, a study of halide-halide exchange at asymmetric silicon was undertaken.

5-2   Halide-halide exchange by mechanism S_N2-Si

In the following reactions, which proceed with predominant inversion of configuration, the entering nucleophile is a stronger base and (for silicon) a better nucleophile than the leaving group X.   Both reactions were carried out in pure, dry chloroform.

$$(+)R_3Si^*Cl + cycloC_6H_{11}NH_3F \longrightarrow$$
$$(+)R_3Si^*F + cycloC_6H_{11}NH_3Cl \qquad (5\text{-}1)$$

$$(+)R_3Si^*Br + cycloC_6H_{11}NH_3Cl \longrightarrow$$
$$(-)R_3Si^*Cl + cycloC_6H_{11}NH_3Br \qquad (5\text{-}2)$$

Reaction (5-1) proceeded with at least 90% inversion of configuration.   Reaction (5-2) proceeded with predominant inversion of configuration, but the stereospecificity was only 82%.

For reaction (5-2), which is homogeneous and is important for discussion in the next section, infrared spectra showed that equimolar concentrations of R_3Si^*Br and $cycloC_6H_{11}NH_3Cl$ give a product which contains a maximum of 2% R_3Si^*Br.   Thus, for the following equilibrium formulation:

$$(+)R_3Si^*Br + cycloC_6H_{11}NH_3Cl \underset{k_r}{\overset{k_f}{\rightleftharpoons}}$$
$$(-)R_3Si^*Cl + cycloC_6H_{11}NH_3Br \qquad (5\text{-}3)$$

it is possible to assign a minimum value for the equilibrium constant which also, of course, provides a ratio for k_f to k_r.   Thus:

$$\frac{k_f}{k_r} = K = \frac{[SiCl][RNH_3Br]}{[SiBr][RNH_3Cl]} = \geq 2.4 \times 10^3$$

A linear plot of $1/C$ versus time for reaction (5-2) during the first half-time was obtained from polarimetric rate data. This gave the second-order rate constant for reaction (5-2) as $k_2 = 6.7$ l. min.$^{-1}$ mole^{-1}. In view of the above equilibrium expression, this means that the second-order rate constant for the backward reaction in (5-3) has a maximum value of $k_2 \leq 2.8 \times 10^{-3}$ l. min.$^{-1}$ mole^{-1}.

5-3 Racemization of R_3Si^*Cl by cyclohexylammonium salts

In Table 5-1 are given the first- and second-order rate constants for the racemization of R_3Si^*Cl by cyclohexylammonium chloride, bromide, and iodide. The rate law for these reactions is rate $= k_2[R_3Si^*Cl][cycloC_6H_{11}NH_3X]$. The racemizations were approximately first order in added salt over the range of 0.04 to 0.09 M salt.

There are two aspects of the data in Table 5-1 which are noteworthy. Firstly, $k_{2(inv.)}$ for racemization of Si*—Cl by RNH_3Br exceeds the rate of displacement of Cl by Br (see Sec. 5-2) by a factor of *at least* 15.

$$\frac{k_{2(inv.)}}{k_{2(displacement)}} = \frac{4.2 \times 10^{-2}}{\leq 2.8 \times 10^{-3}} \geq 15$$

Furthermore, the insensitivity of rate of racemization to variation in the halide-ion component of the salt (less than a factor of 4 is involved) is also quite suggestive.

Table 5-1

Rate-constant data for the racemization of R_3Si^*Cl (0.0872 M) at 25.0° in chloroform with cyclohexylammonium salts (0.0872 M)

Reaction	Halide	$k_{1(rac.)}$ min.$^{-1}$	$k_{2(rac.)}$, l. min.$^{-1}$ mole^{-1}	$k_{2(inv.)}$, l. min.$^{-1}$ mole^{-1}
1	Cl	1.2×10^{-2}	1.4×10^{-1}	6.9×10^{-2}
2	Br	7.2×10^{-3}	8.4×10^{-2}	4.2×10^{-2}
3	I	2.6×10^{-2}	3.0×10^{-1}	1.4×10^{-1}

Taken together, the data suggest operation of an ionization mechanism for racemizations 1, 2, and 3 in Table 5-1.

5-4   Chloride-chloride exchange at asymmetric silicon

Using $cycloC_6H_{11}NH_3Cl^{36}$ in chloroform solvent, it was found that for

$$R_3Si^*Cl + cycloC_6H_{11}NH_3Cl^{36} \rightleftharpoons$$
$$R_3Si^*Cl^{36} + cycloC_6H_{11}NH_3Cl$$

the rate of racemization and the rate of chloride exchange are the same within experimental error. Polarimetric and exchange data were obtained on the same reaction mixture and the agreement in duplicate runs was good. For run 1, $k_{(rac.)}/k_{(ex.)} = 1.1 \pm 0.1$. For run 2, $k_{(rac.)}/k_{(ex.)} = 1.0 \pm 0.1$.

These data are in accord with an ionization S_N1-Si mechanism for the chloride-chloride exchange. In its simplest form, involving formation of a classical dissociated siliconium ion, the mechanism would be written as

$$(+)R_3Si^*Cl \xrightarrow{\text{slow}} R_3Si^+ \text{ (racemic)} \tag{5-4}$$

$$R_3Si^+ \text{ (racemic)} + RNH_3Cl^{36} \xrightarrow{\text{fast}} (\pm)R_3SiCl^{36} \tag{5-5}$$

with the limitation that the Cl^- expelled in (5-4) diffuses into and equilibrates with the medium before recombination of the siliconium ion with chloride ion from the medium. If this limitation is not placed on the mechanism, we could have racemization without exchange, and the rate of racemization should exceed the rate of exchange.

There is a more complex alternative which is more probable, however. It would involve formation of a siliconium ion-pair which: (1) undergoes *fast* retention and inversion exchanges at equal rates, and (2) returns to reactants with retention of configuration. Thus, in the following formulations the rates of formation of $R_3Si^*Cl^{36}$ would be the same by paths (5-6) and (5-7).

$$(+)R_3Si^*Cl \rightleftharpoons (+)[R_3Si]^+[Cl]^- \rightleftharpoons$$
$$(+)[R_3Si]^+[Cl^{36}]^- \rightleftharpoons (+)R_3Si^*Cl^{36} \tag{5-6}$$

$$(+)R_3Si^*Cl \rightleftharpoons (+)[R_3Si]^+[Cl]^- \rightleftharpoons$$
$$(-)[R_3Si]^+[Cl^{36}]^- \rightleftharpoons (-)R_3Si^*Cl^{36} \qquad (5\text{-}7)$$

At the time of writing the present author favors the siliconium ion-pair hypothesis. In this mechanism, formation of the siliconium ion-pair is rate-controlling, and the exchanges, which proceed very rapidly, take place equally fast by retention or inversion of the siliconium ion-pairs.

On this hypothesis racemization of R_3Si^*Cl by RNH_3Br and RNH_3I in chloroform may pursue siliconium ion-pair mechanisms also, except that the composition of the isolated product is, of course, equilibrium-controlled for such fast reactions.

It appears to be true that cyclohexylammonium chloride, bromide, and iodide provide ionization of silicon-chlorine bonds at a rate which can become competitive with S_N2-Si displacement when the anionic part of the salt is not more basic than —Cl. It has been shown that added salts have a very large rate-enhancing effect on carbonium-ion formation in nonpolar media. It has also been found that the rate enhancement produced by salts in such media is frequently approximately first order in added salt.[1]

That the S_N2-Si mechanism greatly predominates over S_N1-Si when Y is more basic than X has been clearly shown by treatment of R_3Si^*Cl with an equimolar mixture of cyclohexylammonium acetate and cyclohexylammonium chloride in chloroform solvent. The product $R_3Si^*OCOCH_3$ was formed in excellent yield and high optical purity with inversion of configuration.[2]

It must not be assumed that chloride-chloride exchange at asymmetric silicon will, in all circumstances, give a ratio of one for $k_{(rac.)}/k_{(ex.)}$. The situation is probably much more complex than that. It is undoubtedly true that a salt such as cyclohexylammonium chloride provides only an exceedingly small concentration of free chloride ion in a nonpolar solvent such as chloroform. In more polar solvents of higher ion-solvating power, which would promote a larger concentration of free chloride ion and would thereby undoubtedly give faster rates by

[1] Cf. S. Winstein, S. Smith, and D. Darwish, J. Am. Chem. Soc., **81,** 5511 (1959), and subsequent papers by Winstein and coworkers.

[2] The data in this chapter comprise very recent work by L. H. Sommer, F. O. Stark, K. W. Michael, and G. A. Parker.

an S_N2-Si mechanism, the classical S_N2 pattern could be observed, i.e., $k_{(rac.)}/k_{(ex.)} = 2.0$. Indeed, it seems probable that an S_N2-Si mechanism and perhaps also an S_N1-Si mechanism (in the less polar media) were operative in some chloride-chloride exchange studies reported for Ph_3SiCl and Et_4NCl[36] in dioxane-nitromethane solvents.[3,*]

[3] A. D. Allen and G. Modena, *J. Chem. Soc.*, 3671 (1957).

* *Added in proof:* For a recent publication on halide-halide exchange at asymmetric silicon, see: L. H. Sommer, F. O. Stark, and K. W. Michael, *J. Am. Chem. Soc.*, **86,** 5683 (1964).

chapter six **Stereochemistry and mechanisms of R$_3$Si*H**

6-1 Introduction

An excellent general review of the chemistry of organosilicon compounds containing Si—H bonds is available and covers the subject until 1959.[1] However, in that review no definitive mechanism formulations could be advanced, owing to lack of necessary data. More recent developments in both kinetics and stereochemistry have shed much light on this aspect of Si—H chemistry. They are discussed in this chapter and in Chap. 8.

6-2 Deuterium-hydrogen exchange with retention of configuration

Optically active R_3Si^*D is readily prepared by reduction of R_3Si^*Cl with lithium aluminum deuteride. R_3Si^*D and R_3Si^*H are easily distinguishable on the basis of their infrared spectra. The deuterosilane has an intense and sharp Si—D absorption band at 6.50 μ, while the Si—H band for R_3Si^*H is at 4.70 μ.

The optically active deuterosilane undergoes deuterium-hydrogen exchange with lithium aluminum hydride at a very slow rate in refluxing ethyl ether. In a di-n-butyl ether solvent with excess lithium aluminum hydride and a reaction temperature of 140°, exchange is much more rapid. After 3 hours, isolation of the product and determination of the infrared spectrum showed that the exchange was about 50% complete.

$$\begin{matrix} (+)R_3Si^*D + LiAlH_4 & \longrightarrow & (+)R_3Si^*H(D) \\ [\alpha]_D\ +34° & & [\alpha]_D\ +34° \end{matrix} \qquad (6\text{-}1)$$

The recovery of $R_3Si^*H + R_3Si^*D$ amounted to 92%. The lack of change in optical rotation proves rigorously that exchange proceeds with retention of configuration. Treatment of R_3Si^*H with lithium aluminum deuteride gave the same results, thus proving that the hydrogen in R_3Si^*H came from the reagent and not from the solvent or from hydrolysis subsequent to reaction.

$$\begin{matrix} (+)R_3Si^*H + LiAlD_4 & \longrightarrow & (+)R_3SiD(H) \\ [\alpha]_D\ +34° & & [\alpha]_D\ +34° \end{matrix} \qquad (6\text{-}2)$$

[1] C. Eaborn, "Organosilicon Compounds," Butterworth & Co. (Publishers), Ltd., London, 1960, chap. 6.

Although the initial reagents in (6-1) and (6-2) are $LiAlH_4$ and $LiAlD_4$, it is not at all certain that these are, in fact, the species responsible for the exchange reactions. After 3 hours at 140°, decomposition is extensive, and much finely divided aluminum is present in the reaction flask:[2]

$$2LiAlH_4 \xrightarrow{\Delta} 2LiH + 2Al + 3H_2$$

In another exchange, a di-*n*-butyl ether solution of lithium aluminum hydride was heated at 140° for 3 hours, and R_3Si^*D was then added and heating continued for an additional 3 hours. The rate of exchange approximated that for (6-1). Stereospecificity was somewhat diminished. The product had $[\alpha]_D +31°$ (ref. 3).

Regardless of whether LiH or $(AlH_4)^-$ or some other Al—H species is responsible for the exchange, the reaction has some interesting general aspects which can be discussed. From a bond-energy standpoint, the exchange is neither exothermic nor endothermic as far as the silicon atom is concerned. Furthermore, the Si—H bond energy is relatively low (76 kcal./mole, see Table 1-6). Nevertheless, the exchange is slow compared to the reductions of R_3Si^*Cl and R_3Si^*OMe, both of which are quite endothermic (with respect to Si) and involve reduction of bonds having relatively high bond energies. The reasons for the slow rate of deuterium-hydrogen exchange are probably at least two in number. Firstly, there is little doubt that displacements of hydride ion from silicon *by bases* are generally slower than corresponding displacements of good leaving groups such as —Cl, —Br, and —OCOR. The latter have rates which are usually too fast to measure by conventional techniques. (Extensive kinetic data are available for the base-catalyzed solvolysis of R_3SiH which gives H_2 and R_3SiO— compounds.) Secondly, unlike leaving groups such as —Cl, —Br, —OMe, and —OCOR, the —H leaving group has no unshared electrons for donation to the electrophilic part of an attacking reagent.

In a solvent such as di-*n*-butyl ether, which is relatively

[2] A. E. Finholt, A. C. Bond, Jr., and H. I. Schlesinger, *J. Am. Chem. Soc.,* **69,** 1199 (1947).

[3] For a preliminary report of this work, see L. H. Sommer and C. L. Frye, *J. Am. Chem. Soc.,* **81,** 1013 (1959).

nonpolar and also has no —OH groups to aid in stabilizing developing negative charge on —H by hydrogen bonding, electrophilic assistance for separation of hydride ion from silicon in the rate-controlling transition state can only be provided by the electrophilic part of the attacking reagent. Also, such assistance can only be rendered at a stage in the reaction process which involves considerable stretching (in the sense: $\overset{\delta^+}{Si} \cdots \overset{\delta^-}{H}$) of the silicon-hydrogen bond, engendered by nucleophilic attack of the base at the silicon atom. All these considerations indicate that the rate-controlling transition state for the deuterium-hydrogen exchange reactions can be represented approximately as follows:

$$
\begin{array}{cc}
\overset{\displaystyle H}{R_3Si\diagdown \diagup AlY_{2\text{-}3}} & \overset{\displaystyle H}{R_3Si\diagdown \diagup Li} \\
D & D
\end{array}
\quad \text{or} \quad
\tag{6-3}
$$

6-3   Retention reactions of R_3Si^*H with oxygen-containing bases[4]

In contrast to the rapid exothermic reaction of powdered potassium hydroxide with R_3Si^*Cl in xylene, reaction of R_3Si^*H with the same reagent in the same solvent required 2 hours of heating at 95°, as indicated by the fact that this period of time elapsed before the evolution of hydrogen gas had ceased. The overall stoichiometry of the reaction is

$$ R_3SiH + KOH \xrightarrow{\text{xylene}} R_3SiOK + H_2 $$

Hydrolysis of the xylene solution of the potassium silanolate gave optically active silanol in 95% yield.

$$
\begin{array}{l}
(+)R_3Si^*H + KOH(s) \xrightarrow[(1)]{} \\
\ [\alpha]_D\ +34° \\
\qquad\qquad (-)R_3Si^*OK \xrightarrow[(2)]{H_2O} (+)R_3Si^*OH \qquad (6\text{-}4) \\
\qquad\qquad\ [\alpha]_D\ -72° \qquad\qquad\ [\alpha]_D\ +17°
\end{array}
$$

---

[4] Discussion in Sec. 6-3 is based on unpublished studies by L. H. Sommer and C. L. Frye; cf. C. L. Frye, Ph.D. Thesis, The Pennsylvania State University, 1960.

The overall conversion of R_3Si*H to R_3Si*OH has a stereospecificity of at least 95% retention of configuration. Thus, the formation of silanolate is highly stereospecific. It is tempting to write a simple four-center representation of the rate-controlling transition state involving simply KOH, and analogous to (6-3). But, recalling again that KOH(s) contains 10 to 12% water, it seems more likely (to this author) that a mechanism analogous to (3-22) may obtain, i.e.,

$$H-\bar{O} \overset{R_3}{\underset{Si}{\nearrow}} \overset{H}{\underset{}{\diagdown}} \quad \longrightarrow \quad HO \overset{R_3}{\underset{Si}{\diagup}} \overset{H}{\underset{}{|}} \quad \longrightarrow \quad R_3SiOK$$

$$\overset{+}{K} \diagup H \qquad \overset{+}{K} \quad H \qquad +$$

$$\underset{|}{\bar{O}} \qquad \qquad \underset{|}{\bar{O}} \qquad \qquad H_2O$$

$$H \qquad \qquad H \tag{6-5}$$

Mechanism (6-5) has the advantage of direct formation of H_2, instead of initial formation of KH followed by reaction with water to give H_2. (The obvious experiment, comparison of rate using anhydrous KOH, has not yet been done.)

A solution of potassium t-butoxide, 0.059 mole, in 65 ml. of dry t-butanol was prepared, and 20 g. of optically active R_3Si*H, 0.08 mole, was added. The reaction mixture was heated at 88 to 92° for 4 hours until evolution of hydrogen ceased. Isolation gave a 97% yield of the t-butoxysilane.

$$(+)R_3Si*H + t\text{-}C_4H_9OH \xrightarrow{KO\text{-}t\text{-}C_4H_9}$$
$$[\alpha]_D +33°$$
$$(-)R_3Si*O\text{-}t\text{-}C_4H_9 \tag{6-6}$$
$$[\alpha]_D -26°$$

The stereospecificity of (6-6) is at least 95% retention of configuration.

It would be highly desirable to be able to determine the stereochemistry of hydride-ion displacement from silicon in polar media such as water or methanol, etc., using bases such as OH^- or MeO^-, but the available evidence indicates that base-catalyzed racemization of R_3Si*OH and $R_3Si*OMe$ in such media might be too fast to permit determination of the steric course of base-catalyzed solvolysis of R_3Si*H in such media. Because of the relatively high steric requirements of the t-butoxy group relative to —H, racemization of R_3Si^*—O-t-C_4H_9 by t-butoxide ion is evidently much slower than the primary reaction.

It has been found[5] that t-butyl alcohol is very poor at dissociating potassium t-butoxide base, that the latter exists in t-butyl alcohol solvent as a solvated ion-pair in which a t-butoxide anion and a t-butyl alcohol molecule are both coordinated with the potassium ion, and that the deuterium-hydrogen exchange of optically active PhEtMeC*D with potassium t-butoxide in t-butyl alcohol (electrophilic substitution at saturated carbon) proceeds with *retention* of configuration because the reagent is able to provide asymmetric solvation of the formed carbanion.

In the light of these facts, an S_Ni-Si retention mechanism for reaction (6-6) is extremely probable.

$$
\begin{array}{c}
\mathrm{R_3} \\
\mathrm{Si} \\
\mathrm{H} \qquad \mathrm{O}\text{-}t\text{-Bu} \\
\mathrm{H} \qquad \mathrm{K} \\
\mathrm{O} \\
t\text{-Bu}
\end{array}
$$

The cyclohexoxy group has steric requirements intermediate between —OMe and —O-t-C_4H_9. In the event, treatment of R_3Si^*H with potassium cyclohexoxide in dry cyclohexanol was interrupted before evolution of hydrogen was complete in order to minimize racemization of the product. The product, obtained after 30 minutes of heating at 82°, was shown to be a mixture of R_3Si^*H and R_3Si^*O-cycloC$_6$H$_{11}$. Since the starting silane was *dextrorotatory* and the product has $[\alpha]_D$ —2°, the predominant stereochemical course was shown to be retention of configuration.

$$(+)R_3Si^*H + cycloC_6H_{11}OH \xrightarrow{\text{KO-cycloC}_6\text{H}_{11}}$$
$$(-)R_3Si^*O\text{-cycloC}_6H_{11} \qquad (6\text{-}7)$$

An S_Ni-Si mechanism is also probable for (6-7).

[5] D. J. Cram, *Chem. Eng. News,* **41,** no. 33, 92 (1963).

6-4   Retention reactions of R_3Si*H with chlorine and bromine

It is an exceedingly interesting fact that the reaction of R_3Si*H with chlorine in carbon tetrachloride solvent is quite fast. At 25°, in carbon tetrachloride solvent, the chlorination of R_3Si*H follows a second-order rate law, rate $= k_2[R_3Si*H][Cl_2]$, which has $k_2 = 2.2 \times 10^2$ l. mole^{-1} min.$^{-1}$ (ref. 6). Bromination in the same solvent is also rapid. The fast reaction rates of R_3Si*H with chlorine and bromine, which are generally regarded as electrophilic reagents in polar reactions, serve to dispose of any naive generalization which assigns fast rates of displacement at silicon solely to the ability of silicon to act as an effective center for nucleophilic attack. In Chap. 8 the importance of two kinds of chemical driving force for organosilicon reactions (electrophilic attack on X and nucleophilic attack on Si) will be emphasized by discussion of quantitative rate studies.

Reaction of R_3Si*H with chlorine gave a 95% yield of optically active chlorosilane.

$$(+)R_3Si*H + Cl_2 \xrightarrow{CCl_4} (-)R_3Si*Cl \tag{6-8}$$

The stereospecificity is at least 97% retention of configuration.

Reaction (6-8) proceeds rapidly in the absence or presence of light and is much faster in carbon tetrachloride than in cyclohexane.

Relative rates data for a reaction series involving a number of different R_3SiH compounds reveal that chlorination of R_3SiH in carbon tetrachloride solvent involves generation of considerable *positive charge* at the silicon atom in the rate-controlling transition state. Thus, $\rho^* = -4.2$ [see Sec. 8-1, reaction series (8-2)]. A second order rate law was found for chlorination and bromination, rate $= k_2[R_3SiH][X_2]$.

Treatment of R_3Si*H with bromine in carbon tetrachloride solvent gave an 85% yield of optically active bromosilane. There is no doubt that the reaction is quantitative, but the sensitivity of R_3Si*Br to atmospheric moisture complicates the handling and isolation of this substance in pure form.

$$(+)R_3Si*H + Br_2 \xrightarrow{CCl_4} (-)R_3Si*Br \tag{6-9}$$

The stereospecificity of (6-9) is at least 97% retention of configuration.

Extensive studies of the mechanism of chlorination and bromination of R_3SiH in carbon tetrachloride[6] solvent yielded the information summarized above and also the very interesting facts indicated in Eq. (6-10).

$$(+)R_3Si^*H + BrCl \xrightarrow{\text{CCl}_4}$$
$$(-)R_3Si^*Br(80\text{–}90\%) + (-)R_3Si^*Cl\ (10\text{–}20\%) \qquad (6\text{-}10)$$

Bromination and chlorination with BrCl proceeded with high stereospecificity, better than 90% retention of configuration. Furthermore, the same ratio of products was found for reaction of Et_3SiH with BrCl, 80 to 90% Et_3SiBr and 10 to 20% Et_3SiCl.

It must be emphasized that there is no evidence that R_3SiBr is not the primary major product in the reactions with BrCl. A solution of triethylbromosilane in carbon tetrachloride was saturated with anhydrous hydrogen chloride, and conversely a solution of triethylchlorosilane in carbon tetrachloride was saturated with anhydrous hydrogen bromide. No halogen exchange was observed in either case. α-NpPhMeSi*H was reacted with an excess of bromine chloride, and, after the initial extremely fast reaction, no significant change in rotation occurred. Also, Speier has shown[7] that bromine chloride reacts with Me_3SiCl to give $(BrCH_2)Me_2SiCl$ without conversion of Si—Cl to Si—Br.

Finally, the order of reactivity of the halogenation reagents is

$$BrCl \gg Cl_2 > Br_2$$
$$130 \qquad 8 \qquad 1$$

White and Robertson[8] have reported the following order of reactivity for Br_2 and BrCl in a study of the third-order kinetics of halogen additions to olefins in acetic acid:

$$BrCl \gg Br_2$$
$$400 \qquad 1$$

[6] L. H. Sommer and N. C. Lloyd, unpublished studies.

[7] J. L. Speier, *J. Am. Chem. Soc.*, **73**, 826 (1951); J. L. Speier, Brit. Pat. 683, 460; *Chem. Abstr.*, **48**, 1419e (1964).

[8] E. P. White and P. W. Robertson, *J. Chem. Soc.*, 1508 (1939).

Taken together, all the facts concerning reaction of R_3SiH with BrCl, Cl_2, and Br_2 suggest that the mechanism involves formation of a three-center intermediate which decomposes rapidly to products with retention of configuration. This is shown below for reaction of R_3Si^*H with BrCl.

$$R_3Si^*H + BrCl \xrightarrow{slow} \left[R_3Si^* \overset{\oplus}{\underset{Br}{\overset{H}{\diagdown}}} \right] \cdots Cl^{\ominus}$$

(6-11)

$$\left[R_3Si^* \overset{\oplus}{\underset{Br}{\overset{H}{\diagdown}}} \right] \cdots Cl^{\ominus} \xrightarrow{fast} R_3Si^*Br + HCl$$

Because of the polarity in the Br—Cl molecule, $\overset{\delta^+}{Br}\!\!-\!\!\overset{\delta^-}{Cl}$, and its known mode of reaction as positive Br and negative Cl, a simple four-center mechanism, S_Ni-Si, for reaction of R_3Si^*H with BrCl would be expected to yield mainly R_3Si^*Cl. This is not observed.

Mechanism (6-11) is difficult to classify. On a formal basis it involves electrophilic displacement at silicon and is an example of a three-center S_Ei-Si mechanism. But the fact that $Br^{\oplus}$ has unshared pairs of electrons for donation to Si in the postulated intermediate no doubt contributes to the stability and formation of that intermediate. This is indicated by the fact that R_3SiD does *not* undergo deuterium-hydrogen exchange with HBr in carbon tetrachloride solution. The following intermediate does *not* form:

$$\left[R_3Si \overset{\oplus}{\underset{D}{\overset{H}{\diagdown}}} \right] \cdots Br^{\ominus}$$

On balance, therefore, it seems best to designate the mechanism for reactions of R_3SiH with BrCl, Cl_2, and Br_2 in carbon tetrachloride as $(S_Ni\text{-}S_Ei)$-Si. The postulated intermediate has the unit positive charge distributed over three atoms and is in accord with $\rho^* = -4.2$ for chlorination. It is certainly in accord with very clean retention of configuration. It is consistent with formation of R_3SiBr as the major product with BrCl. It is consistent with greatly increased rates for BrCl relative to Cl_2 and Br_2. It is consistent with second-order kinetics.

6-5   A retention reaction of R_3Si^*H with perbenzoic acid[9]

Treatment of optically active R_3Si^*H with excess perbenzoic acid in benzene solvent at room temperature for 12 hours gave a 40% yield of optically active R_3Si^*OH.

$$(+)R_3Si^*H + C_6H_5COOOH \longrightarrow$$
$$[\alpha]_D \ +34°$$

$$(+)R_3Si^*OH + C_6H_5CO_2H \qquad (6\text{-}12)$$
$$[\alpha]_D \ +18°$$

The stereospecificity of (6-12) is at least 90% retention. It should be pointed out that this interesting reaction does *not* give the benzoxysilane as the primary product, despite the fact that perbenzoic acid is usually considered to be a source of $[C_6H_5CO_2]^-$ and $[OH]^+$ in polar reactions. Considerable experimentation has shown that (6-12) correctly represents the reaction course.

The mechanism for (6-12) may be analogous to the $(S_Ni\text{-}S_Ei)$-Si mechanism proposed for chlorination and bromination of R_3Si^*H.

$$R_3Si^*H + C_6H_5CO_3H \xrightarrow{\text{slow}} \left[R_3Si^{*\oplus} \overset{\displaystyle H}{\underset{\displaystyle O-H}{\diagup}} \right] \cdots C_6H_5CO_2^{\ominus}$$

$$\left[R_3Si^{*\oplus} \overset{\displaystyle H}{\underset{\displaystyle O-H}{\diagup}} \right] \cdots C_6H_5CO_2^{\ominus} \xrightarrow{\text{fast}} R_3Si^*OH + C_6H_5CO_2H$$

6-6   Summary of stereochemistry and mechanisms of R_3Si^*H

Table 6-1 summarizes the stereochemical facts and mechanism postulates discussed in this chapter.

[9] Unpublished recent work of L. H. Sommer and G. A. Parker.

Table 6-1
Stereochemistry and mechanisms of R_3Si*H

Reactant	Reagent	Solvent	Product	Stereo-chemistry	Mechanism
$(+)R_3Si*D$	$LiAlH_4$	Bu_2O	$(+)R_3Si*H$	Ret.	S_Ni-Si
$(+)R_3Si*H$	$LiAlD_4$	Bu_2O	$(+)R_3Si*D$	Ret.	S_Ni-Si
$(+)R_3Si*H$	$KOH(s)$	xylene	$(-)R_3Si*OK$	Ret.	S_Ni-Si
$(+)R_3Si*H$	$KO\text{-}t\text{-}C_4H_9$	$t\text{-}C_4H_9OH$	$(-)R_3Si*O\text{-}t\text{-}C_4H_9$	Ret.	S_Ni-Si
$(+)R_3Si*H$	$KO\text{-}cycloC_6H_{11}$	$cycloC_6H_{11}OH$	$(-)R_3Si*O\text{-}cycloC_6H_{11}$	Ret.	S_Ni-Si
$(+)R_3Si*H$	Cl_2	CCl_4	$(-)R_3Si*Cl$	Ret.	$(S_Ni\text{-}S_Ei)$-Si
$(+)R_3Si*H$	Br_2	CCl_4	$(-)R_3Si*Br$	Ret.	$(S_Ni\text{-}S_Ei)$-Si
$(+)R_3Si*H$	$BrCl$	CCl_4	$(-)R_3Si*Br$	Ret.	$(S_Ni\text{-}S_Ei)$-Si
$(+)R_3Si*H$	$C_6H_5CO_3H$	CCl_4	$(+)R_3Si*OH$	Ret.	$(S_Ni\text{-}S_Ei)$-Si

chapter
seven **Relative and absolute configurations of α-naphthylphenylmethyl-silanes**

7-1   Introduction

For purposes of convenient reference Table 7-1, an abbreviated version of Table 2-1, can serve as the basis for discussion of correlations of configuration. The order of listing has been changed to accord with the order in which correlations are discussed in the present chapter.

7-2   Chemical correlations of configuration

Following the classical method of chemical correlations of configuration used in organic chemistry to relate carbon-oxygen compounds, compounds I to VIII were shown to have the same configuration through use of $(-)R_3Si^*OK$. The latter was prepared from $(+)R_3Si^*OH$ with either potassium hydroxide or potassium metal, and hence the *dextrorotatory* silanol and the *levorotatory* silanolate have the same configuration of the asymmetric silicon atom; the conversion to silanolate proceeds without attack at the asymmetric silicon. Reactions of II with dimethyl sulfate and with RCOCl compounds yielded enantiomers III to VII; see (3-2) through (3-6). All these syntheses are unlikely to involve the asymmetric center. Independent evidence for the validity of that conclusion comes from the isolation of *dextrorotatory* silanol as a by-product in lithium aluminum hydride reductions of $(+)R_3Si^*OCOR$ compounds, as the result of

Table 7-1
Enantiomers having the $(+)R_3Si^*H$ configuration

Compound no.	Compound structure and sign of $[\alpha]_D$	Compound no.	Compound structure and sign of $[\alpha]_D$
I	$(+)R_3Si^*OH$	IX	$(+)R_3Si^*H$
II	$(-)R_3Si^*OK$	X	$(+)R_3Si^*F$
III	$(+)R_3Si^*OMe$	XI	$(-)R_3Si^*Cl$
IV	$(+)R_3Si^*OCOCH_3$	XII	$(-)R_3Si^*O\text{-}cycloC_6H_{11}$
V	$(+)R_3Si^*OCOC_6H_5$	XIII	$(-)R_3Si^*Br$
VI	$(+)R_3Si^*OCOC_6H_4(NO_2)\text{-}p$	XIV	$(-)R_3Si^*O\text{-}t\text{-}C_4H_9$
VII	$(+)R_3Si^*OCOC_6H_3(NO_2)_2\text{-}3,5$	XV	$(-)R_3Si^*\text{-}(-)OMen$
VIII	$(+)R_3Si^*OSi^*R_3$	XVI	$(+)R_3Si^*Et$

carbonyl reduction competitive with reduction at silicon [see (3-28) and (3-32)]. The methyl groups in dimethyl sulfate are effective centers for nucleophilic attack, and it is not possible to write a reasonable mechanism for conversion of II to III which would involve cleavage of the silicon-oxygen bond in R_3Si^*OK. The conversion of II to optically active VIII upon reaction with $(+)R_3Si^*Cl$, and the formation of *meso*-disiloxane from II and $(-)R_3Si^*Cl$, rigorously correlate the configuration of VIII with that of II [see (4-13) and (4-14)].

It is not possible to prepare enantiomers XII, XIV, and XV from $(-)R_3Si^*OK$. For example, cyclohexyl halides and cyclohexyl tosylate failed to give the cyclohexoxysilane with the silanolate. Instead, the silanolate functioned as a base for removal of HX from these substances.

Although direct chemical correlations of configuration are not possible for cases in which the terminal atom of the functional group directly attached to silicon is changed, we may here advance some arguments, based on chemical reasoning, which point to the validity of the correlation for some of those cases. For example, consider the following stereochemical equations:

$$(+)R_3Si^*Cl + NaBH_4 \longrightarrow (+)R_3Si^*H$$
$$(+)R_3Si^*Cl + NaB(OMe)_4 \longrightarrow (+)R_3Si^*OMe$$

In both reactions the source of the entering group is $(BY_4)^-$. Barring an extraordinary degree of stereochemical complexity, it is reasonable to assume that the stereochemical course is the same in both reactions; especially in view of the fact that $(BH_4)^-$ and $[B(OMe)_4]^-$ are essentially nucleophilic reagents, contain saturated tetracovalent boron, and are negatively charged. Assumption of a common stereochemical course for both reactions leads to assignment of the same configuration to III and IX.

Demonstration of an inversion stereochemistry for the reaction of R_3Si^*OTs with R_3Si^*OK (see Sec. 3-7) and consideration of the fact that $-OTs$ and $-Cl$ are both excellent leaving groups lead to the reasonable assumption that the reaction of R_3Si^*Cl with R_3Si^*OK also involves inversion of configuration. If that conclusion is correct, then from the stereochemical equation

$$(+)R_3Si^*Cl + (-)R_3Si^*OK \xrightarrow{\text{inversion}} (+)R_3Si^*OSi^*R_3$$

it would follow that $(+)R_3Si^*OSi^*R_3$ and $(+)R_3Si^*Cl$ have opposite configurations, and that correlation of *dextrorotatory* disiloxane with *levorotatory* chlorosilane, as given in Table 7-1, is correct.

Pursuing the leaving-group reasoning a bit further, we can consider the fact that chemical correlations of configuration prove that the reactions of R_3Si^*Cl follow a common stereochemical course with the following diverse reagents: H_2O, MeOH, KOH(s), $Hg(OAc)_2$, $NaB(OMe)_4$, cyclo$C_6H_{11}NH_3OCOC_6H_5$, R_3Si^*OK, etc. Now, the dramatic change in stereochemistry which occurs with the change from a poor leaving group, such as —OMe, to a good leaving group, such as —$OCOC_6H_5$, indicates that the reaction of methanol with $R_3Si^*OCOC_6H_5$ (known to be inversion from chemical correlations of configuration) parallels the stereochemical path for methanolysis of R_3Si^*Cl. Thus, we again arrive at the conclusion that $(-)R_3Si^*Cl$ is correctly correlated in Table 7-1. (In the argument just made, the terms "poor" and "good" refer to relative reaction rates with basic reagents.)

7-3   X-ray application of the Fredga method

One of the most widely used techniques for correlating configurations of optically active compounds having *similar* structures is the Fredga method based on *differences in phase behavior*.[1] This technique seemed ideal for comparison of the crystalline compounds R_3Si^*H, R_3Si^*F, and R_3Si^*Cl. The great structural similarity for these three compounds is obvious. The changes in structure amount to replacement of only one atom by another, while keeping the carbon-silicon arrangement constant in molecules containing 17 carbon atoms.

The Fredga method as applied by K. Mislow has provided many fruitful results in recent years, and the pertinent case observed for the R_3Si^*— compounds is his "Case 2" (ref. 2). In

---

[1] See A. Fredga in: "The Svedberg, Almqvist and Wikesells," Uppsala, 1944, p. 261. J. Timmermans, *J. Chim. Phys.,* **49,** 162 (1952). Conclusions drawn on the basis of a *difference* in phase behavior have proved accurate without exception.

[2] K. Mislow and M. Heffler, *J. Am. Chem. Soc.,* **74,** 3668 (1952). For a recent application of "Case 2" for determination of the configurational relationships between the pure optical isomers of 3-thioloctanedioic acid and 3-methyloctanedioic acid, see K. Mislow and W. C. Meluch, *ibid.,* **78,** 5920 (1956). For other examples see J. Timmermans, *loc. cit.*

this type of application of the Fredga method, pure optical isomers of two different substances that are isomorphous give solid solutions when they are of the same configuration, and a eutectic when they are of opposite configuration. For R_3Si^*H, R_3Si^*F, and R_3Si^*Cl, x-ray diffraction provided clear and consistent answers:[3]

1. Solid solutions are formed by $(-)R_3Si^*H$ and $(-)R_3Si^*F$; by $(-)R_3Si^*F$ and $(+)R_3Si^*Cl$; and by $(-)R_3Si^*H$ and $(+)R_3Si^*Cl$.

2. Eutectic mixtures are formed by $(-)R_3Si^*H$ and $(+)R_3Si^*F$; by $(+)R_3Si^*F$ and $(+)R_3Si^*Cl$; and by $(+)R_3Si^*H$ and $(+)R_3Si^*Cl$.

Optically active R_3Si^*H, R_3Si^*F, and R_3Si^*Cl crystallize individually in the orthorhombic system with space group $P2_12_12_1$; an example of perfect isomorphism is observed. The three mixtures (1) also crystallize in the orthorhombic system and are isomorphous with the pure component compounds; no doubling of the unit cell dimensions or change in the symmetry is observed. In Table 7-2 the crystallographic constants for the pure and mixed crystals are listed.

By comparing the intensities of diffracted x-rays from the mixed crystals (1) with those from the pure component crystals, it is concluded that a random distribution of the component molecules in the crystal is observed for each mixture in (1).

[3] The x-ray data in Tables 7-2 and 7-3 were kindly furnished by Y. Okaya and R. Pepinsky, Department of Physics, The Pennsylvania State University.

Table 7-2

Crystallographic constants of the pure and mixed crystals

Crystal	a	b	c	Space group
$(-)R_3Si^*H$	8.80	20.19	8.00	$P2_12_12_1$
$(-)R_3Si^*F$	8.80	19.85	8.00	$P2_12_12_1$
$(-)R_3Si^*Cl$	8.84	19.68	8.10	$P2_12_12_1$
$(-)R_3Si^*H + (-)R_3Si^*F^d$	9.00	20.22	8.15	$P2_12_12_1$
$(-)R_3Si^*H + (+)R_3Si^*Cl^d$	8.85	20.20	8.20	$P2_12_12_1$
$(-)R_3Si^*F + (+)R_3Si^*Cl^d$	8.82	19.80	8.40	$P2_12_12_1$

^{d} These data are for equimolar mixtures.

Table 7-3
Partial list of reflections used for criteria

| Reflections | For $(-)R_3Si^*H + (-)R_3Si^*F$ | | |
	$(-)Si^*H$	Mixture	$(-)Si^*F$
080	st	m	w
600	st	m	w
120	vw	m	st
330	m	w	abs

| Reflections | For $(-)R_3Si^*H + (+)R_3Si^*Cl$ | | |
	$(-)Si^*H$	Mixture	$(+)Si^*Cl$
0,10,2	v st	m	vw
0,11,2	vw	w	m

| Reflections | For $(-)R_3Si^*F + (+)R_3Si^*Cl$ | | |
	$(-)Si^*F$	Mixture	$(+)Si^*Cl$
080	w	m	st
0,10,0	st	m	vw

v st = very strong, st = strong, m = medium, w = weak,
vw = very weak, and abs = too weak to be observed.

A partial list of the two-dimensional reflections used for the criteria is given in Table 7-3.

At this point, with the aid of the correlations of configuration arrived at through use of x-ray application of the Fredga method, it is possible to support correlations of configuration for compounds I to XI in Table 7-1, through the use of some very direct arguments. Thus, we may consider the following stereochemical equations:

$$(-)R_3Si^*Cl + KOH(s) \longrightarrow (+)R_3Si^*OK$$
$$(+)R_3Si^*H + KOH(s) \longrightarrow (-)R_3Si^*OK$$

It is clear that assignment of the same configuration to $(-)R_3Si^*Cl$ and $(+)R_3Si^*H$ indicates that KOH(s) gives opposite stereochemical paths with —Cl, a good leaving group, compared to —H, a poor leaving group. From previous discussion it is also clear that, on the basis of a *difference* in stereochemistry, the logical choice is an inversion path for —Cl and a retention path for —H. In turn, that choice supports the assignment of the same configuration to $(-)R_3Si^*Cl$ and $(-)R_3Si^*OK$ in Table 7-1. Furthermore, in view of chemical correlations of configuration, this means that $(-)R_3Si^*Cl$ is correctly correlated with compounds I to VIII in Table 7-1.

Further support for correlation of $(-)R_3Si^*Cl$ and $(-)R_3Si^*OK$ can be obtained from consideration of the following stereochemical equations:

$$(+)R_3Si^*Cl + H_2O \longrightarrow (+)R_3Si^*OH$$
$$(+)R_3Si^*OH + LiAlH_4 \longrightarrow (+)R_3Si^*H$$

Since $(+)R_3Si^*Cl$ and $(+)R_3Si^*H$ have opposite configurations based on the Fredga correlation, it is clear that hydrolysis of R_3Si^*Cl and reduction of R_3Si^*OH follow opposite stereochemical paths. Based on a *difference* in stereochemistry, the logical choice is inversion for hydrolysis of R_3Si^*Cl and retention for reduction of R_3Si^*OH. That choice supports assignment of the same configuration to $(-)R_3Si^*Cl$ and $(+)R_3Si^*OH$ in Table 7-1.

Additional support for assignment of the same configuration to $(-)R_3Si^*Cl$ and $(-)R_3Si^*OK$ is provided by the following stereochemical equations:

$$(+)R_3Si^*Cl + MeOH \longrightarrow (+)R_3Si^*OMe$$
$$(+)R_3Si^*OMe + LiAlH_4 \longrightarrow (+)R_3Si^*H$$

Once again the net result of a two-step process is inversion of configuration, and the logical choice, based on a *difference* in stereochemistry for the two reactions, is inversion for methanolysis of R_3Si^*Cl and retention for reduction of R_3Si^*OMe. From that choice it follows that $(-)R_3Si^*Cl$ and $(+)R_3Si^*OMe$ have the same configuration and are correctly correlated in Table 7-1. Furthermore, $(+)R_3Si^*OMe$ and $(-)R_3Si^*OK$ have the same configuration based on chemical correlations of configuration.

Assignment of the same configuration to $(-)R_3Si^*Cl$ and $(-)R_3Si^*OK$ and the postulate of a common inversion stereochemistry for reactions of R_3Si^*Cl with diverse nucleophilic reagents correctly predict the following stereochemical equation:

$$(-)R_3Si^*Cl + (-)R_3Si^*OK \longrightarrow meso\text{-}R_3Si^*OSi^*R_3$$

Correlation of configuration for compound XII in Table 7-1 is provided by the following stereochemical equations:

$$(+)R_3Si^*Cl + cycloC_6H_{11}OH \longrightarrow (-)R_3Si^*O\text{-}cycloC_6H_{11}$$
$$(-)R_3Si^*O\text{-}cycloC_6H_{11} + LiAlH_4 \longrightarrow (+)R_3Si^*H$$

A *difference* in stereochemistry is evident, and the choice of inversion for cyclohexanolysis and retention for reduction of $(-)R_3Si^*O\text{-}cycloC_6H_{11}$ leads to assignment of the same configuration to $(-)R_3Si^*Cl$, $(-)R_3Si^*O\text{-}cycloC_6H_{11}$, and $(+)R_3Si^*H$.

Assignment of the same configuration to $(-)R_3Si^*Cl$ and $(-)R_3Si^*Br$ in Table 7-1 is based on formation of the same enantiomers from reactions of the two *levorotatory* halides with water, methanol, lithium aluminum hydride, and other nucleophilic reagents, and on the fact that —Br like —Cl is a good leaving group.

Correlation of configuration for compound XIV in Table 7-1 is provided by the following stereochemical equations:

$$(+)R_3Si^*Cl + KO\text{-}t\text{-}C_4H_9 \longrightarrow (-)R_3Si^*O\text{-}t\text{-}C_4H_9$$
$$(-)R_3Si^*O\text{-}t\text{-}C_4H_9 + LiAlH_4 \longrightarrow (+)R_3Si^*H$$

The choice of inversion for the reaction of R_3Si^*Cl with $KO\text{-}t\text{-}C_4H_9$ and retention of configuration for reduction of the *t*-butoxysilane leads to assignment of the same configuration to $(-)R_3Si^*Cl$, $(-)R_3Si^*\text{—}O\text{-}t\text{-}C_4H_9$, and $(+)R_3Si^*H$.

Correlation of configuration for compound XV in Table 7-1 is indicated by the following stereochemical equations:

$$(-)R_3Si^*Cl + (-)MenOH \longrightarrow (+)R_3Si^*\text{—}(-)OMen$$
$$(+)R_3Si^*\text{—}(-)OMen + LiAlH_4 \longrightarrow (-)R_3Si^*H$$

The choice of inversion for the reaction of $(-)MenOH$ with R_3Si^*Cl and retention for the reduction of the menthoxysilane leads to assignment of the same configuration to $(-)R_3Si^*Cl$, $(-)R_3Si^*\text{—}(-)OMen$, and $(+)R_3Si^*H$.

The main argument for assignment of the $(+)R_3Si^*H$ configuration to $(+)R_3Si^*Et$ derives from consideration of the following stereochemical equations:

$$(+)R_3Si^*OMe + EtMgBr \longrightarrow (+)R_3SiEt$$
$$(+)R_3Si^*Cl + EtLi \longrightarrow (+)R_3Si^*Et$$

Based on assignment of opposite configurations for $(+)R_3Si^*OMe$ and $(+)R_3Si^*Cl$, it is evident that opposite stereochemical paths are indicated for the reactions of R_3Si^*OMe and R_3Si^*Cl with EtMgBr and EtLi, respectively. The logical choice of retention for the reaction of R_3Si^*OMe and inversion for R_3Si^*Cl leads to assignment of the same configuration for $(-)R_3Si^*Cl$, $(+)R_3Si^*Et$, and $(+)R_3Si^*H$.

7-4   Optical rotatory dispersion

In Fig. 7-1 are shown optical rotatory dispersion curves for compounds I, III, IV, IX, X, and XI in Table 7-1. It is interesting that these six enantiomers, having the same assigned configuration, also have the same sign of rotation between 375 and 340 mμ.

The shapes of plain dispersion curves have been used previously to correlate configurations of optically active compounds having closely similar structures. In the case of $(+)$-α-(p-iodophenoxy)-propionic acid, $(+)$-α-(m-iodophenoxy)-propionic acid, and $(-)$-α-(o-iodophenoxy)-propionic acid, all three optical isomers have a $(+)$ sign of rotation at ca. 325 mμ, and independent evidence from plant physiological tests confirms assignment of the same configuration to all three.[4]

However, as has been pointed out by Djerassi,[5] correlation between rotatory dispersion curves and configuration must take into account the possibility of free-rotational "conformational" isomerization. Examination of accurately scaled molecular models clearly shows that the hydrogen atom on the naphthalene nucleus in the peri position relative to the silicon atom in the R_3Si^*X compounds causes considerable "crowding" in its imme-

---

[4] Cf. C. Djerassi, "Optical Rotatory Dispersion," McGraw-Hill Book Company, New York, 1960, pp. 236–237.

[5] Reference 4, pp. 102–108.

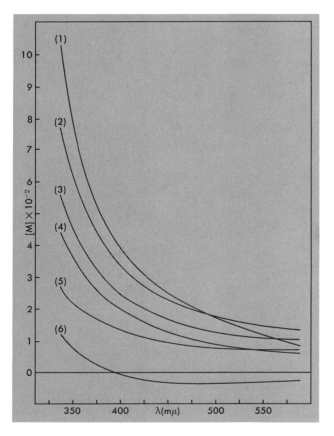

Fig. 7-1   Rotatory dispersion curves for R_3Si^*X:
(1), $(+)R_3Si^*OH$;   (2), $(+)R_3Si^*F$;   (3), $(+)R_3Si^*H$;
(4), $(+)R_3Si^*OCH_3$;   (5), $(+)R_3Si^*OCOCH_3$;   (6), $(-)R_3Si^*Cl$.

diate vicinity.   Maximum freedom of intramolecular motions is attained when the *peri*-hydrogen is flanked by the two groups of the remaining three that have the smallest steric requirements. Five of the six compounds in Fig. 7-1 have a functional group whose steric requirements (for "crowding" about the *peri*-hydrogen) are distinctly smaller than those of the methyl group and hence should have approximately the same "conformation" distributions.   The fact that the sixth compound, $(-)R_3Si^*Cl$, has a functional group only slightly smaller than methyl, and yet is correctly correlated with $(+)R_3Si^*H$ and $(+)R_3Si^*F$ (paralleling results from the Fredga method),[3] is evidence that the correlations of configuration implied by all six curves are valid.[6]

7-5   Absolute configurations

A recent report on the application of rigorous x-ray methods to the problem of absolute configurations for optically active α-naphthylphenylmethylsilanes shows that the *dextrorotatory* R_3Si^*H and R_3Si^*F have the configuration shown below:[7]

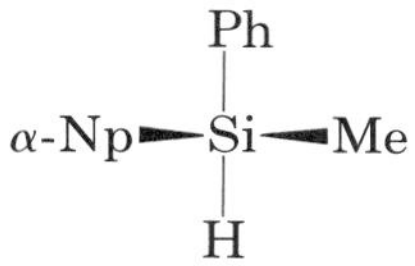

Ph   Ph

α-Np—Si—Me   α-Np—Si—Me

H   F

$(+)R_3Si^*H$ 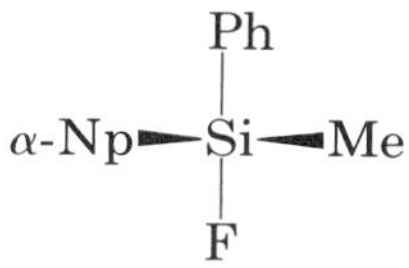 $(+)R_3Si^*F$

These studies confirm the results of application of the Fredga method to the relative configurations of R_3Si^*F and R_3Si^*H, and, in combination with correlations in Table 7-1, provide the absolute configurations of many optically active organosilicon compounds.[8,*]

[6] A cutoff point of 340 mμ in the optical rotatory dispersion curves in Fig. 7-1 avoids the hazard of possible errors introduced by incursion of high absorbance due to the naphthyl group at lower wavelengths.

[7] T. Ashida, R. Pepinsky, and Y. Okaya, Abstracts, International Union of Crystallography Congress, Rome, Italy, September, 1963.

[8] Application of Cram's rule of asymmetric induction [D. J. Cram and F. A. Abd Elharez, *J. Am. Chem. Soc.,* **74,** 5828 (1952)], plus some reasonable assumptions as applied to the addition of MeMgBr to R_3Si^*COPh, has also led to the above assignment of absolute configuration for $(+)R_3Si^*H$ [A. G. Brook and W. W. Limburg, *ibid.,* **85,** 832 (1963)].

* *Added in proof:* For a very recent publication on correlations of configuration for R_3Si^*X, see: L. H. Sommer, C. L. Frye, G. A. Parker, and K. W. Michael, *J. Am. Chem. Soc.,* **86,** 3271 (1964).

chapter eight **Structure and reactivity**

8-1 Introduction

In previous chapters we have noted that the dynamic stereochemistry of R_3Si^*X is sensitive to the nature of X, the reagent, and the solvent. In this chapter, which deals with quantitative aspects of structure-reactivity relationships, we shall again note the sophisticated nature of the silicon atom in the sensitivity of reaction rate to polar and steric effects of the organic substituents, the nature of X, the reagent, and the solvent. In a general way, this chapter provides further evidence for the existence of a wide range of polar mechanisms for organosilicon reactions.

Like other studies of this kind (especially in the field of physical organic chemistry), the quantitative treatment of relative rates in this chapter makes extensive use of the Hammett and Taft equations:

$$\log \frac{k}{k_0} = \sigma\rho$$

$$\log \frac{k}{k_0} = \sigma^*\rho^*$$

An excellent detailed treatment of the Hammett and Taft equations and their use in physical organic chemistry is available.[1]

For purposes of subsequent discussion in this chapter, it is important to note that reaction constants ρ and ρ^* for S_N2 displacements at saturated carbon have small values, of the order of -1.0. Reaction constants ρ and ρ^* have large negative values for S_N1 carbonium-ion reactions, of the order of -3.0. Reaction constants ρ and ρ^* have large positive values for base-catalyzed hydrolysis of organic esters, of the order of $+3.0$. Negative ρ or ρ^* indicates that electron-releasing substituents enhance rate. Positive ρ or ρ^* indicates that electron-withdrawing substituents enhance rate.

A large negative value of ρ or ρ^* is generally taken to indicate generation of a significant positive charge at the reaction center in the transition state. A large positive ρ or ρ^* indicates that the reaction center acquires considerable negative charge in the transition state.

[1] R. W. Taft, Jr., in M. S. Newman, "Steric Effects in Organic Chemistry," John Wiley & Sons, Inc., New York, 1956, chap. 13.

For a reaction series in which the only variable is change in the substituents attached to the reaction center, deviation from the linear Hammett and Taft relationships may provide a quantitative measure of steric effects in special cases not subject to resonance interaction between the substituent and the reaction center. In such cases the following special Taft equation applies:

$$\log \frac{k}{k_0} = E_s + \sigma^* \rho^*$$

in which E_s is a steric substituent constant. Substituent constant σ^* is a measure of the polar effect of a substituent, and its value is independent of the nature of the reaction series. E_s is a measure of the steric effect of a substituent, and its value depends upon the particular reaction series under investigation. Large values for E_s in a particular reaction series indicate that steric effects are large in that reaction series.

8-2   Polar and steric effects of substituents

An excellent example of wide variation in the polar effects of substituents on organosilicon rates is provided by the values of ρ^* for two reaction series involving R_3SiH compounds.

$$R_3SiH + R'OH + R'O^- \xrightarrow{R'OH}$$
$$R_3SiOR' + H_2 + R'O^- \qquad (8\text{-}1)$$

$$R_3SiH + Cl_2 \xrightarrow{CCl_4} R_3SiCl + HCl \qquad (8\text{-}2)$$

For (8-1), an extended reaction series covering a variation in rate constant of 10^4 gave $\rho^* = +4.3$. For (8-2), an extended reaction series covering a variation in rate constant of 10^5 gave $\rho^* = -4.2$.

Reaction series (8-1) is for reaction of R_3SiH with 0.04 to 1.9 N potassium hydroxide in aqueous alcohol containing 93.7 wt. % ethanol at 0° (ref. 2). Reaction series (8-2) comprised reaction of R_3SiH with 10^{-4} to 10^{-2} M chlorine in carbon tetrachloride at $27 \pm 2°$ (ref. 3).

[2] O. W. Steward and O. R. Pierce, *J. Am. Chem. Soc.*, **83**, 1916 (1961).

[3] L. H. Sommer and N. C. Lloyd, unpublished studies; see N. C. Lloyd, Ph.D. Thesis, The Pennsylvania State University, 1962.

Table 8-1
Second-order rate constants for (8-1) and (8-2)

No.	R	R'	R''	$k_{2(8-1)}$, l. mole^{-1} min.$^{-1}$	$k_{2(8-2)}$, l. mole^{-1} min.$^{-1}$	$\dfrac{k_{2(8-1)}}{k_{2(8-2)}}$
1	CH_3	CH_3	CH_3	2.8×10^{-2}	1.3×10^3	2.2×10^{-5}
2	$CH_3CH_2CH_2$	CH_3	CH_3	1.2×10^{-2}	3.9×10^3	3.1×10^{-6}
3	$CF_3CH_2CH_2$	CH_3	CH_3	9.9×10^{-1}	6.3×10^1	1.6×10^{-2}
4	$CF_3CH_2CH_2$	$CF_3CH_2CH_2$	CH_3	2.6×10^1	2.8	9.3
5^a	$CF_3CH_2CH_2$	$CF_3CH_2CH_2$	$CF_3CH_2CH_2$	6.2×10^2	2.7×10^{-1}	2.3×10^3

^{a} The value for $k_{2(8-1)}$ was calculated from no. 4, using $\rho^* = +4.3$ and σ^* for $CF_3CH_2CH_2$ as $+0.32$.

Representative data in Table 8-1 illustrate the dramatic difference in the polar effects of substituents on rate for the two reaction series. Both reactions follow a second-order rate law, i.e.,

$$-\frac{d[R_3SiH]}{dt} = k_2[R_3SiH][R'O^-] \qquad (8\text{-}3)$$

$$-\frac{d[R_3SiH]}{dt} = k_2[R_3SiH][Cl_2] \qquad (8\text{-}4)$$

In the original paper,[2] a good straight-line correlation plot for log (k/k_0) vs. $\Sigma\sigma^*$ included a total of 14 R_3SiH compounds, all having closely similar steric requirements of the R groups. The slope of the best line for all 14 compounds gave $\rho^* = +4.3$ for reaction series (8-1). For reaction series (8-2) an excellent straight-line correlation plot was also obtained.

In connection with the demonstration of variable reaction constants ρ^* for reaction series involving R_3SiH rates, it is interesting to discuss a third reaction series. This involved determination of the first-order rate constants for acid-catalyzed solvolysis of R_3SiH in 95 vol. % ethanol at 34.8°.

$$R_3SiH + R'OH_2^+ + R'OH \longrightarrow$$
$$R_3SiOR' + H_2 + R'OH_2^+ \qquad (8\text{-}5)$$

For the entire reaction series the reagent was 1.43 N HCl in the designated solvent.[4]   Eleven R_3SiH compounds gave a good straight-line correlation plot with a slope corresponding to $\rho^* = +0.77$.   All these contained primary R groups.   The solvents used in (8-1) and (8-5) are very similar, and both reactions comprise solvolysis of R_3SiH to give H_2 and R_3SiOR'.   Nevertheless, the change from base to acid catalysis brings about a very significant change in the susceptibility of rate to polar effects of substituents.   Thus, for (8-1) the ratio of rate constants for $(CF_3CH_2CH_2)_2MeSiH$ and $(CH_3CH_2CH_2)Me_2SiH$ is 2.2×10^3.   For (8-5) the corresponding ratio is 2.6.

If we choose a compound whose substituents have low polarity, e.g., $(CH_3CH_2CH_2)Me_2SiH$, we can obtain a rough measure of the effectiveness of base versus acid catalysis for such a special case.   At the same concentrations of KOH and HCl, after rough correction for the difference in reaction temperature, $k_1(KOH)/k_1(HCl)$ amounts to about 10^2.

It is interesting to inquire concerning the relative steric effects of substituents in reaction series (8-1), (8-2), and (8-5).   A measure of the steric effects of $i\text{-}C_3H_7$ and $t\text{-}C_4H_9$ substituents on rate would be the deviation of the actual $\log (k/k_0)$ values from the best correlation line used to obtain ρ^*.   From a reaction series very similar to (8-1),[5] the deviations for $(i\text{-}C_3H_7)Me_2SiH$, $(i\text{-}C_3H_7)_2MeSiH$, $(i\text{-}C_3H_7)_3SiH$, and $(t\text{-}C_4H_9)Me_2SiH$ are respectively -0.42, -0.82, -1.1, and -1.87 log units.[5]   These values give an average E_s constant for a single $i\text{-}C_3H_7$ substituent in (8-1) as -0.40, and $E_s = -1.87$ for a single $t\text{-}C_4H_9$ substituent, according to the Taft equation:[6]

$$\log \frac{k}{k_0} = E_s + \sigma^*\rho^*$$

[4] O. W. Steward and O. R. Pierce, *J. Am. Chem. Soc.,* **83,** 4932 (1961).

[5] Data for $i\text{-}C_3H_7$ and $t\text{-}C_4H_9$ substituents are not given in ref. 2. The reaction series used to estimate steric effects involved 95 vol. % ethanol at 34.5° and KOH. From rate data for six silanes containing unsubstituted primary alkyl groups, the best correlation line gave $\rho^* = +3.5 \pm 0.2$ [L. H. Sommer and W. P. Barie, Jr., unpublished work; see W. P. Barie, Jr., Ph.D. Thesis, The Pennsylvania State University, 1954]. In ref. 2, the best correlation line for unsubstituted primary alkyl substituents also gave $\rho^* = +3.5$.

[6] R. W. Taft, Jr., in M. S. Newman, "Steric Effects in Organic Chemistry," John Wiley & Sons, Inc., New York, 1956, chap. 13.

Table 8-2
Reaction constants and E_s parameters for (8-1) and the base-catalyzed hydrolysis of $RCOOC_2H_5$

Reaction	Constant ρ^*	Parameter	
		$E_s(i\text{-}C_3H_7)$	$E_s(t\text{-}C_4H_9)$
Base-catalyzed $RCOOC_2H_5$ hydrolysis	+2.48	−0.47	−1.54
Base-catalyzed R_3SiH solvolysis	+4.3	−0.40	−1.87

The steric substituent constants E_s were calculated from the rate data using $\rho^* = +3.5$.

It is extremely interesting to compare ρ^* and E_s for (8-1) with ρ^* and E_s for the well-known base-catalyzed hydrolysis of esters, RCOOR, whose mechanism is known to involve an addition complex as a reaction intermediate. For closely similar solvent systems, the relevant parameters are given in Table 8-2.

In reaction series (8-5), rate data for $(i\text{-}C_3H_7)_3SiH$ are available for comparison with silanes having primary organic groups. Use of the Taft equation gives an average E_s steric substituent constant for a single $i\text{-}C_3H_7$ group in this series as $E_s = -0.34$. [Data for a $t\text{-}C_4H_9$ substituent are not available for series (8-5).] Thus, steric effects in (8-1) and (8-5) appear to be closely similar in magnitude. It is extremely interesting that the same is true for comparison of acid- and base-catalyzed hydrolysis of organic esters.[6] There is a further analogy which involves ρ^*. The latter is much greater for base-catalyzed than for acid-catalyzed hydrolysis of esters.[6]

For reaction series (8-2), rate data for $(i\text{-}C_3H_7)_3SiH$ in comparison with silanes having primary organic groups gave an E_s steric substituent parameter for a single $i\text{-}C_3H_7$ group in this series as $E_s = -0.42$. Thus, despite a large negative ρ^*, steric effects in this series are considerable.

We turn now to the discussion of rate studies of some R_3SiO— compounds. The convenient study of polar and steric effects of substituents on rates of R_3SiOR' solvolysis required that (1) the rates be slow enough for application of ordinary techniques, and (2) that a physical method be applicable. Both requirements were met by the choice of R_3Si—(−)OMen, optically active menthoxysilanes, for study. These compounds have the structure

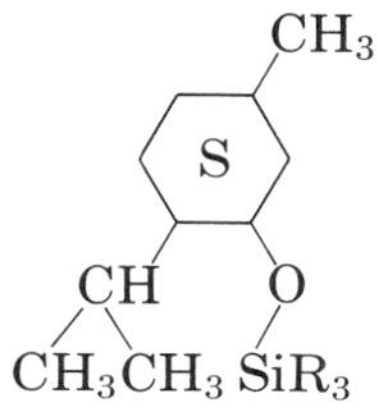

CH$_3$

S

CH   O

CH$_3$CH$_3$ SiR$_3$

I

From I it is clear that menthoxy is a secondary group and that the isopropyl substituent can provide considerable steric hindrance to reaction at the silicon center. Furthermore, the menthoxy group is optically active, and the change in optical rotation resulting from solvolysis provides a convenient physical method for studying rates.

It was found that the use of a methanol solvent at 25° allowed studies to be made of base- and acid-catalyzed rates of methanolysis of the menthoxysilanes. Thus, two reaction series were obtained:[7]

$$R_3SiOR^* + MeOH + MeO^- \longrightarrow$$
$$R_3SiOMe + R^*OH + MeO^- \qquad (8\text{-}6)$$

$$R_3SiOR^* + MeOH + MeOH_2^+ \longrightarrow$$
$$R_3SiOMe + R^*OH + MeOH_2^+ \qquad (8\text{-}7)$$

Since methanol is present in large excess, the reactions go to completion in the forward direction. Also, both series follow a second-order rate law: first order in R_3SiOR^* and first order in basic or acidic catalyst.

$$-\frac{d[R_3SiOR^*]}{dt} = k_2[R_3SiOR^*][MeO^-] \qquad (8\text{-}8)$$

$$-\frac{d[R_3SiOR^*]}{dt} = k_2[R_3SiOR^*][MeOH_2^+] \qquad (8\text{-}9)$$

For (8-6) the added basic catalyst was sodium methoxide. For (8-7), a buffer system of equimolar pyridine–pyridine hydrochloride was used to obtain the low methylonium-ion concentra-

[7] L. H. Sommer, J. H. Markillie, and F. O. Stark; see J. H. Markillie, M.S. Thesis, The Pennsylvania State University, 1959.

Table 8-3
Rate constants for base- and acid-catalyzed solvolysis of RR'R''SiOR*

No.	R	R'	R''	$k_{2(8-6)}$, l. mole^{-1} min.$^{-1}$	$k_{2(8-7)}$, l. mole^{-1} min.$^{-1}$	$\dfrac{k_{2(8-7)}}{k_{2(8-6)}}$
1	CH_3	CH_3	CH_3	0.785	8.41×10^4	1.07×10^5
2	C_2H_5	C_2H_5	C_2H_5	6.06×10^{-4}	1.32×10^3	2.18×10^6
3	$i\text{-}C_3H_7$	CH_3	CH_3	1.30×10^{-3}	9.75×10^2	7.47×10^5
4[a]	$i\text{-}C_3H_7$	$i\text{-}C_3H_7$	$i\text{-}C_3H_7$		0.11	
5	C_6H_5	CH_3	CH_3	2.17	7.24×10^4	3.34×10^4
6	C_6H_5	C_6H_5	C_6H_5	7.48×10^{-1}	2.19×10^2	2.28×10^2
7	$\alpha\text{-Np}$	C_6H_5	CH_3	0.13	4.99×10^2	3.84×10^3
8	$\alpha\text{-Np}$	$C_6H_4(CF_3)\text{-}m$	CH_3	1.77	1.59×10^2	8.98×10^1

[a] Reaction with base was too slow to measure: no detectable reaction with 1.168 N NaOMe after several hours.

tion necessary for following rate. Representative data are given in Table 8-3.

Comparison of compounds 7 and 8 served to provide values of ρ for the two reaction series. The use of a *meta* —CF_3 substituent was deliberate. This substituent has a σ determined only by its inductive contribution; resonance contribution to σ for this substituent[6] is 0.00, and the possible complication of resonance interaction between the substituent and Si across the phenyl ring was thereby avoided. The Hammett equation and a value for meta —CF_3 of $\sigma = +0.415$ (ref. 6) gives

$$\log \frac{k}{k_0} = +0.415\rho$$

From this the rate-constant data for 7 and 8 gave $\rho = +2.7$ for reaction series (8-6), and $\rho = -1.2$ for reaction series (8-7).

From the Taft equation and the reasonable assumption that ρ and ρ^* are closely similar in value,[6] we may calculate E_s steric substituent constants for C_2H_5 and $i\text{-}C_3H_7$ groups in both reaction series, relative to CH_3 as a standard: i.e., $E_s = 0.00$ for CH_3. For a single ethyl substituent using data for compounds 1 and 2: $E_s = -0.78$ for series (8-6); $E_s = -0.72$ for series (8-7). For a single isopropyl substituent using data for compounds 1 and 3: $E_s = -2.27$ for series (8-6); $E_s = -2.17$ for series (8-7). The near-quantitative additive relationship for steric effects is demon-strated by calculation of the total steric effect of three isopropyl groups (relative to methyl) from data for compounds 1 and 4 in series (8-7) and then division by 3 to give E_s for a single isopropyl group. This gives $E_s = -2.19$, compared to $E_s = -2.17$ obtained from rate data for 1 and 3.

Comparison of steric effects in reaction series (8-1) and (8-5) with those in (8-6) and (8-7) is interesting. Firstly, it is clear that steric effects for acid- and base-catalyzed solvolysis of R_3SiOR^* are closely similar. The same is true of (8-1) and (8-5). Secondly, steric effects are much greater in (8-6) and (8-7).

In (8-1) and (8-5), Me_3SiH and $(C_2H_5)_3SiH$ have rates which are nicely correlated by the Taft equation, $\log (k/k_0) = \sigma^*\rho^*$, indicating that the steric effects of methyl and ethyl groups in these series are the same: i.e., E_s for ethyl is zero. In (8-6) and (8-7) the E_s value for ethyl exceeds that for isopropyl in (8-1) and (8-5) by about -0.3 log units. For the former series, the E_s value of isopropyl exceeds that for t-butyl in (8-1) by about -0.3 log units. In short, the change from —H, a small leaving group of simple structure, to —OMen, a large leaving group of large steric requirements in the neighborhood of the Si, causes a profound increase in the steric effects of substituents on rate.

In (8-6) and (8-7), despite the similarity of steric effects for the two series, the change from acid- to base-catalyzed solvolysis makes ρ considerably more positive. The same is true of ρ^* for comparison of (8-1) and (8-5). The effect on ρ or ρ^* engendered by the change in the catalyst is placed in proper perspective when it is compared with the corresponding change from acid- to base-catalyzed hydrolysis of organic esters. For the latter, ρ^* becomes more positive by 2.48 units. For (8-1) and (8-5), ρ^* changes by 3.53 units. For (8-6) and (8-7), the change is 3.9 units.

The complication of d_π-p_π bonding between phenyl groups and silicon makes discussion of the rate data for compounds 5 and 6 quite hazardous, at least from the standpoint of E_s and ρ^*. It is likely that the apparent σ^* value for phenyl is a sensitive function of reactant and reagent structure. Thus, we cannot calculate E_s for phenyl with any degree of confidence. This type of uncertainty should not obtain for comparison of compounds 7 and 8 for the purpose of calculating ρ.

The change in ρ^* observed for the change from acid- to base-catalyzed redistribution of siloxanes (involving cleavage and re-formation of Si—O—Si linkages which lead to preparation of "silicone" polymers) is very important from a chemical process standpoint. Directionally, the change is the same as for the solvolysis reactions already discussed. The order of decreasing reactivity toward bases is as follows:[8]

$$(Me_2SiO)_4 > Me_3Si(OSiMe_2)_2OSiMe_3$$
$$> Me_3SiOSiMe_2OSiMe_3 > (Me_3Si)_2O \qquad (8\text{-}10)$$

Thus, for base-catalyzed redistribution the accumulation of electronegative oxygen substituents facilitates rate. On the other hand, acid-catalyzed redistribution gives the following reactivity order:[9]

$$(Me_3Si)_2O > (Me_2SiO)_4 \qquad (8\text{-}11)$$

Quantitative data suitable for calculation of actual ρ^* and E_s values are not available. It is interesting that acid- and base-catalyzed redistribution of a given siloxane mixture comes to the same equilibrium point. The composition of the product mixture is thus equilibrium-controlled, and desired polymer compositions can be prepared by suitable choice of starting materials in the proper ratio, without regard to the type of catalyst employed.

Kinetics of polymerization of octamethylcyclotetrasiloxane by KOH(s) at 120–160° have been studied.[10] At equilibrium, 94% of the starting material is polymerized to —$OSiMe_2(OSiMe_2)_xO$— species, and the rate of polymerization is proportional to the concentration of $(Me_2SiO)_4$ and to the square root of the initial concentration of KOH(s). The latter aspect of the rate law is interesting and deserves some discussion. It has been explained[10] in the following way: (1) The KOH(s) rapidly dissolves in the siloxane with formation of $\equiv$SiOK, and potassium silanolate was found to have the same catalytic activity as KOH(s). (2) Conductivity studies show that $\equiv$SiOK is little

[8] S. W. Kantor, W. T. Grubb, and R. C. Osthoff, *J. Am. Chem. Soc.*, **76**, 5190 (1954).

[9] D. W. Scott, *J. Am. Chem. Soc.*, **69**, 2294 (1946).

[10] W. T. Grubb and R. C. Osthoff, *J. Am. Chem. Soc.*, **77**, 1405 (1955).

ionized in siloxane media.[11]   (3) In view of (1) and (2), the following equations apply:[10]

$$\equiv SiOK \; \rightleftharpoons \; \equiv SiO^- + K^+$$

and the ionization equilibrium must lie well over toward $\equiv SiOK$. This leads to the equilibrium expression:

$$K = \frac{[\equiv SiO^-][K^+]}{[\equiv SiOK]} = \frac{[\equiv SiO^-]^2}{[\equiv SiOK]}$$

Now, since all the KOH(s) is converted to silanolate,

$$K = \frac{[\equiv SiO^-]^2}{[KOH]}$$

Furthermore, polymerization takes place by attack of a silanolate ion on a siloxane linkage, thus leading to the rate law

$$\text{Rate} = k[\equiv SiO^-][(Me_2SiO)_4]$$

From the last two equations it is evident that

$$\text{Rate} = k \times K^{1/2}[KOH]^{1/2}[(Me_2SiO)_4] \qquad (8\text{-}12)$$

The condensation of silanols to siloxanes is important for the formation of "silicone" polymers:

$$2\equiv Si{-}OH \; \longrightarrow \; \equiv Si{-}O{-}Si\equiv + H_2O \qquad (8\text{-}13)$$

and we turn now to a discussion of polar and steric factors as they affect the rates of (8-13). The kinetics and equilibria of the condensation of Me_3SiOH in methanol solvent have been studied.[12]   The technique used involved titration with Karl-Fischer reagent toward which one Si—OH bond and one molecule of water are equivalent. As the condensation proceeds, the

[11] D. T. Hurd, R. C. Osthoff, and M. L. Corrin, *J. Am. Chem. Soc.,* **76,** 249 (1954).

[12] W. T. Grubb, *J. Am. Chem. Soc.,* **76,** 3408 (1954).

quantity of reagent used decreases toward a limit of one-half the amount required at the start of the reaction.

$$2Me_3SiOH \longrightarrow (Me_3Si)_2O + H_2O \qquad (8\text{-}14)$$

In actual fact, the condensation does not take the simple course indicated by (8-14). Instead, an equilibrium between silanol and methoxysilane is rapidly established (8-15); siloxane formation results from reaction of methoxysilane with silanol (8-16).

$$Me_3SiOH + MeOH \rightleftharpoons Me_3SiOMe + H_2O \qquad (8\text{-}15)$$
$$Me_3SiOH + Me_3SiOMe \rightleftharpoons Me_3SiOSiMe_3 + MeOH \qquad (8\text{-}16)$$

The solvent-reactant methanol is, of course, present in large excess, and this displaces equilibrium (8-15) in the forward direction to such an extent that substantially all the silanol is removed from the system at equilibrium. Siloxane formation in equilibrium (8-16) is not complete, and equilibrium concentrations are correlated by the expression:

$$K = \frac{[(Me_3Si)_2O]}{[Me_3SiOMe]^2[H_2O]} \qquad (8\text{-}17)$$

The approach to equilibrium is catalyzed by bases and by acids, and the equilibrium attained is independent of the type of catalyst used. Various experiments established that the rate of siloxane formation is first order in silanol, Me_3SiOMe, and catalyst.

$$\frac{d[(Me_3Si)_2O]}{dt} = k_3[Me_3SiOH][Me_3SiOMe][Me_3SiO^-] \qquad (8\text{-}18)$$

$$\frac{d[(Me_3Si)_2O]}{dt} = k_3[Me_3SiOH][Me_3SiOMe][MeOH_2^+] \qquad (8\text{-}19)$$

The similarity of Eqs. (8-8) and (8-18) is evident, as is also that between Eqs. (8-9) and (8-19). The following observed facts relative to Me_3SiOH condensation[12] constitute further points of similarity: (1) Acid catalysis gives faster rates than base catalysis; at equivalent concentrations of potassium hydroxide and hydrochloric acid the latter gives rates that are faster by a factor of 500. (2) Steric effects of substituents appear to be quite large; $(C_6H_5)_3SiOH$ and $(C_2H_5)_3SiOH$ have relative acid-catalyzed rates, compared to Me_3SiOH as a standard, that are 10^{-6} and 1.6×10^{-3}, respectively; compounds such as $(t\text{-}C_4H_9)Me_2SiOH$ (ref. 13) and $(t\text{-}C_4H_9)_2Si(OH)_2$ (ref. 13) have extraordinary stability and are resistant to condensation by either acid or base.

A study of the kinetics of solvolysis of trialkylphenoxysilanes in 51.4 wt. % ethanol-water medium at 25° was made,[14] and is of interest for comparison with the alkoxysilane solvolyses already discussed. Like the latter, solvolysis of $R_3SiOC_6H_5$ is acid- and base-catalyzed. At the neutral point of a phosphate buffer, the first-order rate constant for solvolysis of $Me_3SiOC_6H_5$ is ca. 10^{-5} sec.$^{-1}$. At a hydrogen-ion concentration of 0.01 M the rate constant increases to ca. 0.1 sec.$^{-1}$, and at a similar concentration of $R'O^-$ it is ca. 3.3 sec.$^{-1}$ ($R' = H$ or C_2H_5).

$$R_3SiOC_6H_5 + R'OH + R'O^- \longrightarrow$$
$$R_3SiOR' + C_6H_5O^- + R'OH \qquad (8\text{-}20)$$

$$R_3SiOC_6H_5 + R'OH + ROH_2^+ \longrightarrow$$
$$R_3SiOR' + C_6H_5OH + R'OH_2^+ \qquad (8\text{-}21)$$

In (8-20) and (8-21), changes in pH engendered by phenol formation are balanced by buffer action. The rates are first order in $R_3SiOC_6H_5$ and first order in catalyst.

$$-\frac{d[R_3SiOC_6H_5]}{dt} = k_2[R_3SiOC_6H_5][RO^-]$$

$$-\frac{d[R_3SiOC_6H_5]}{dt} = k_2[R_3SiOC_6H_5][R'OH_2^+]$$

Table 8-4 gives the second-order rate constants for base- and acid-catalyzed solvolysis of the phenoxysilanes. Calculations assuming equal E_s steric substituent constants for C_2H_5 and for $t\text{-}C_4H_9$ in series (8-20) and (8-21) indicate that the *difference* in

[13] L. H. Sommer and L. J. Tyler, *J. Am. Chem. Soc.*, **76**, 1030 (1954).

[14] E. Akerman, *Acta Chem. Scand.*, **10**, 298 (1956).

Table 8-4
Second-order rate constants for base- and acid-catalyzed solvolysis of $R_3SiOC_6H_5$

No.	R_3Si	$k_{2(8-20)}$, l. mole^{-1} sec.$^{-1}$	$k_{2(8-21)}$, l. mole^{-1} sec.$^{-1}$	$\dfrac{k_{2(8-20)}}{k_{2(8-21)}}$
1	Me_3Si	~330	10.4	32
2	$(C_2H_5)_3Si$	2.1	0.22	9.6
3	$(n\text{-}C_3H_7)_3Si$	0.66	0.12	5.5
4	$(n\text{-}C_4H_9)_3Si$	0.41	0.082	5.1
5	$(n\text{-}C_5H_{11})_3Si$	0.33	0.060	5.0
6	$(t\text{-}C_4H_9)Me_2Si$	1.72×10^{-2}	5.9×10^{-4}	29

ρ^* for these two series is less than the corresponding difference for (8-8) and (8-9). Without further data it is not possible to evaluate individual ρ^* and E_s constants for the phenoxysilane series. However, even if we assume a large positive value of ρ^* for series (8-20), say $\rho^* = +4.0$, the steric substituent constant for a single $t\text{-}C_4H_9$ group would still be $E_s = -2.8$. Thus, steric effects are very large in both (8-20) and (8-21). We may also note that rate constants for base-catalyzed solvolysis are larger than acid-catalyzed rates for the phenoxysilanes, whereas the reverse is true for alkoxysilane solvolysis. This point receives further comment below.

We turn next to a discussion of the polar and steric effects of substituents on the rates of silicon-halogen reactions. The sparse data available for R_3SiCl solvolysis have already been discussed in Sec. 4-1. (This was done for the purpose of making clear the very fast rates of these reactions prior to discussion of the stereochemistry of R_3Si^*Cl.) In brief, steric effects of substituents were found to be large. But the available data do not permit accurate evaluation of ρ^* or E_s constants.

The rates of hydrolysis of R_3SiF compounds are much slower than those of R_3SiCl. In comparison to the rate constant for Ph_3SiCl with 2 M water in acetone, $k_1 = 4.0$ sec.$^{-1}$ at 25°, the rate constant for Ph_3SiF with 50% aqueous acetone (ca. 25 M water) was reported[15] to be 1.1×10^{-5} sec.$^{-1}$ at 45°. Since the rates for Ph_3SiCl were reported to be higher than first

[15] C. G. Swain, R. M. Estere, Jr., and R. H. Jones, *J. Am. Chem. Soc.*, **71**, 965 (1949).

order in [H$_2$O], a conservative estimate of k_1(Ph$_3$SiCl)/k_1(Ph$_3$SiF) would be seven powers of ten for hydrolysis in 50% aqueous acetone. The relatively slow rates of hydrolysis of R$_3$SiF compounds, compared to R$_3$SiCl, R$_3$SiBr, and R$_3$SiI, make possible the study of R$_3$SiF hydrolyses by a conventional kinetics technique involving titration of aliquots for formed fluoride ion under conditions which do not result in significant reaction of R$_3$SiF during the time needed for titration.[15]

In their study of the hydrolysis rates of triphenyl- and tri-*p*-tolylfluorosilane, Swain and coworkers reported that in 50% aqueous acetone at 45° the reactions proceeded to completion.[15] In fact, the latter conclusion is incorrect. During the course of an extensive series of studies on the hydrolysis of R$_3$SiF compounds,[16] it was found that the hydrolysis of Ph$_3$SiF in 50% aqueous acetone at 45° comes to equilibrium at 69% reaction. However, the rate constant obtained in the later work was the same as that previously reported to within 10%. The early portion of the first-order plots is quite linear for Ph$_3$SiF.

Experimentally, the work with neutral aqueous acetone solutions at 45° imposed some difficulties. Evaporation of the solvent at 45° altered the relative concentrations of the components unless rate studies were carried out in sealed ampoules, and, in addition, the neutral reactions were quite slow. At 25° the evaporation problem was not as serious, but many fluorosilanes were not sufficiently soluble in the medium, and the rates were very slow. During these preliminary studies it was found, confirming earlier preliminary work,[17] that acid catalysis of rate is quite pronounced. By changing the solvent from 50% aqueous acetone to 66.7% aqueous acetone (66.7 vol. % acetone and 33.3 vol. % water) and using added nitric acid as a catalyst, the reactions proceeded at convenient rates, and the fluorosilanes were sufficiently soluble at 25°.

The equilibrium character of the hydrolysis of R$_3$SiF in aqueous acetone has some interesting aspects which perhaps deserve some discussion. Hydrolysis of 0.0100 *M* Ph$_3$SiF at 25° in the new solvent, 66.7% aqueous acetone containing 19.19 *M*

[16] L. H. Sommer and M. C. Musolf, unpublished work; see M. C. Musolf, Ph.D. Thesis, The Pennsylvania State University, 1960.

[17] L. H. Sommer and N. S. Marans, unpublished work; see N. S. Marans, M.S. Thesis, The Pennsylvania State University, 1947.

water, came to equilibrium at 74% hydrolysis ($K_{eq.} \times [H_2O] = 0.020$). When the reverse reaction was studied using 0.0100 M Ph$_3$SiOH and 0.0100 M HF, 78% of the added hydrofluoric acid remained unreacted at equilibrium ($K_{eq.} \times [H_2O] = 0.027$). A threefold increase of the silanol concentration resulted in a shift in the equilibrium position to 47% hydrofluoric acid remaining unreacted ($K_{eq.} \times [H_2O] = 0.022$); and when the concentration of hydrofluoric acid was increased threefold, the equilibrium was shifted to 84% acid remaining ($K_{eq.} \times [H_2O] = 0.027$). These experiments and others with Ph$_3$SiF and other R$_3$SiF compounds indicate quite clearly that for many cases hydrolysis yields an equilibrium system

$$R_3SiF + H_2O \rightleftharpoons R_3SiOH + HF$$

for which the equilibrium constant

$$K_{eq.} = \frac{[R_3SiOH][HF]}{[R_3SiF][H_2O]}$$

varies between the limits of 10^{-2} to 10^{-4}.

Since very few studies of structure-equilibrium relationships are available for organosilicon reactions, it is of some interest to tabulate and comment on the equilibria for R$_3$SiF hydrolysis.[16]

The polar effects of substituents upon the equilibrium constants for hydrolysis can be seen from the data obtained for two sets of compounds; in each set steric factors are the same. The ratio of the equilibrium constant of γ-chloropropyl-i-propylmethylfluorosilane to that of n-butyl-i-propylmethylfluorosilane was 1.6 and that of m-trifluoromethylphenyldiphenylfluorosilane to triphenylfluorosilane was 5.7. From these two ratios it is evident that the equilibrium constants for the hydrolysis are increased by electron-withdrawing groups and are about as sensitive to polarity changes as the ionization of carboxylic acids. It is also of interest to consider the effect of steric hindrance on the equilibrium constants. By comparing the equilibrium constants for the last six compounds in Table 8-5 it is seen that the constants vary only by a factor of 8, even though the steric requirements of the substituents vary a great deal. Thus, steric effects on the forward and backward rates are closely similar.

Table 8-5

Equilibrium constants for fluorosilane hydrolysis in 66.7% aqueous acetone at 24.9°

Compound	$K_{eq.} \times [H_2O] \times 10^3$	Compound	$K_{eq.} \times [H_2O] \times 10^3$
Ph_3SiF	23	$n\text{-}Bu_3SiF$	0.7
$(m\text{-}CF_3C_6H_4)(Ph_2)SiF$	130	$i\text{-}Pr_3SiF$	5
$(\alpha\text{-}Np)(Ph)(Me)SiF$	4	Et_2MeSiF	2.8
$(CH_2{=}CH)_3SiF$	120	$(\gamma\text{-}ClPr)(i\text{-}Pr)(Me)SiF$	2.1
Et_3SiF	1.1	$(n\text{-}Bu)(i\text{-}Pr)(Me)SiF$	1.3

Studies of the hydrolysis of alkyl fluorides,[18] substituted benzyl fluorides,[19] and benzoyl fluoride[20] have shown that these hydrolyses are acid-catalyzed. In this respect the hydrolyses of R_3SiF resemble those of C—F compounds as is readily apparent from the data of Table 8-6.

[18] N. B. Chapman and J. L. Levy, *J. Am. Chem. Soc.*, 1673, 1677 (1952).
[19] W. T. Miller, Jr., and J. Bernstein, *J. Am. Chem. Soc.*, **70**, 3600 (1948).
[20] C. W. L. Bevan and R. F. Hudson, *J. Chem. Soc.*, 2187 (1953).

Table 8-6

Acid catalysis of Ph_3SiF hydrolysis in 66.7% aqueous acetone at 24.9°

Initial molar concentration of Si—F	Molar concentration of HNO_3	$k_{obs.} \times 10^2$ min.$^{-1}$	$\dfrac{k_{obs.}}{[HNO_3]}$	m^a
0.0105	0.0000	0.00343		
0.0105	0.0063	0.228	0.363	
0.0050	0.0300	1.12	0.373	
0.0050	0.0300	1.16	0.386	
0.0100	0.0300	0.943	0.314	
0.0100	0.0300	0.899	0.300	
0.0105	0.0314	1.27	0.404	
0.0105	0.0300	0.993	0.331	
0.0150	0.0300	0.879	0.293	
0.0105	0.0628	2.14	0.341	
0.0105	0.1578	5.27	0.335	1.0
			Avg. 0.34 ± 0.03	

^{a} m is the slope of the line obtained from a plot of log $k_{obs.}$ vs. log $[HNO_3]$ and corresponds to the order of the reaction with respect to added mineral acid. Relative to nitric acid, the HF formed during the course of hydrolysis is apparently far less effective for acid catalysis. The latter acid must be a far poorer source of hydronium ions in the reaction medium used.

Table 8-7

Rate constants for acid-catalyzed fluorosilane hydrolysis in 66.7% aqueous acetone at 24.9°

Compound	$\dfrac{k_{obs.}}{[HNO_3]}$, l. mole^{-1} min.$^{-1}$	m^a
i-Pr$_3$SiF	0.017^b	1.1
n-Bu$_3$SiF	1.0	0.88
Et$_3$SiF	2.5	0.93
Et$_2$MeSiF	>10^c	
(n-Bu)(i-Pr)(Me)SiF	1.5	1.2
(γ-ClPr)(i-Pr)(Me)SiF	2.0	0.92
Ph$_3$SiF	0.34	1.0
(m-CF$_3$C$_6$H$_4$)(Ph)$_2$SiF	0.75	1.0
(m-CF$_3$C$_6$H$_4$)$_3$SiF	>10	
(α-Nap)(Ph)(Me)SiF	0.21	1.4
(CH$_2$=CH)$_3$SiF	>10	

^{a} Order to which the concentration of added nitric acid appears in the rate expression.

^{b} The $k_{obs.}$ values are taken from the linear portions of the first-order rate plots, before the reverse reaction has become significant.

^{c} The titration technique used imposes the limitation of minimum values for the fast reactions.

Rate constants for a series of eleven R$_3$SiF compounds are listed in Table 8-7.

$$R_3SiF + H_2O + H_3O^+ \longrightarrow R_3SiOH + HF + H_3O^+$$

$$(8\text{-}22)$$

In that table it can be seen that the order of the hydrolysis in added nitric acid is usually near 1.0. Actually, the average order was 1.0 with an average deviation of 0.1. Values of m were determined by varying [HNO$_3$] from 0.005 to 0.16 M. Determination of the true order of the reaction with respect to [H$_2$O] in a system such as 66.7% aqueous acetone is virtually impossible because of serious medium changes which accompany significant changes in [H$_2$O]. In one series of experiments the order in [H$_2$O] was found to be 1.3; however, the water concentration was only varied by a factor of 1.7. For the data given in Table 8.7, which must reflect formation of a transition state having a net formal positive charge resulting from the presence of one proton and one or more molecules of H_2O plus R_3SiF, it is extremely interesting to note that ρ is positive. The ratio of the rates for $(m\text{-}CF_3C_6H_4)(Ph_2)SiF$ and Ph_3SiF corresponds to $\rho = +0.82$. The rate data for $(\gamma\text{-}ClPr)(i\text{-}Pr)(Me)SiF$ and $(n\text{-}Bu)(i\text{-}Pr)(Me)SiF$ correspond to $\rho^* = +0.52$. These data clearly show that electron-withdrawing substituents facilitate rate. The same conclusion was reached by Swain and coworkers on the basis of their work in initially neutral 50% aqueous acetone at 45°, based on rate constants for triphenyl- and tri-p-tolylfluorosilane which were reported[15] to be 7.0×10^{-4} and 1.3×10^{-4} min.$^{-1}$, respectively. If steric effects of R were not important for rate, the change from Et_3SiF to $i\text{-}Pr_3SiF$ should, on the basis of σ^* values and the Taft equation, correspond to a rate decrease of less than a factor of 2. The actual rate decrease, a factor of about 120, indicates a considerable sensitivity of the rate of hydrolysis to the steric requirements of R. Relative to C_2H_5 as a standard, E_s for $Et \equiv 0.00$, the average steric substituent constant for a single $i\text{-}C_3H_7$ group is -0.72. E_s for $i\text{-}C_3H_7$ could not be evaluated for series (8-22) because data for Et_2MeSiF comprise only a lower limit for the actual rate. Nevertheless, it is clear that E_s for $i\text{-}C_3H_7$ in (8-22) must reflect greater steric effects in (8-22) than in (8-1) and (8-2).

We turn next to a discussion of the polar and steric effects of substituents on the rates of certain silicon-alkyl reactions. The first of these involves the solvolysis of $R_3SiCH_2CH_2Cl$ compounds in ethanol-water media without added base or acid.

$$R_3SiCH_2CH_2Cl + R'OH \longrightarrow$$
$$R_3SiOR' + CH_2{=}CH_2 + HCl \qquad (8\text{-}23)$$

These reactions follow a first-order rate law.

$$-\frac{d[R_3SiCH_2CH_2Cl]}{dt} = k_1[R_3SiCH_2CH_2Cl] \qquad (8\text{-}24)$$

Investigation of polar and steric effects was performed using an ethanol-water medium containing 70 vol. % ethanol at 50.0°. Relative rates for five β-chloroethylsilanes are given in Table 8-8 (ref. 21).

[21] L. H. Sommer and G. L. Baughman, unpublished work; see G. L. Baughman, Ph.D. Thesis, The Pennsylvania State University, 1961.

Table 8-8
Structural effects on initially neutral solvolysis rates of $R_3SiCH_2CH_2Cl$ in 70% ethanol at 50.0°

R_3Si-	k/k_0
Me_3Si	1.000^a
$(C_2H_5)_2MeSi$	0.955
$(i-C_3H_7)Me_2Si$	0.652
$(C_6H_5)Me_2Si$	0.0955
$(m-CF_3C_6H_4)Me_2Si$	0.0123

^{a} For the standard compound $Me_3SiCH_2CH_2Cl$, $k_1 = 1.78 \times 10^{-3}$ sec.$^{-1}$.

Calculation of the Hammett reaction constant using rate constants for the two aryl silanes in Table 8-8 gave $\rho = -2.15$. Thus, electron-donating groups greatly facilitate rate in reaction series (8-23).

Calculation of steric substituent constants assuming $\rho^* = \rho = -2.15$ gave $E_s = -0.23$ for a single ethyl group; $E_s = -0.59$ for a single isopropyl group. Steric factors for reaction series (8-23) probably result from *steric hindrance to solvation of a developing cationic charge at the silicon atom.*

Polar and steric effects of substituents for a series similar to (8-23) are of interest. This involves the acid-catalyzed solvolysis of $R_3SiCH_2CH_2OH$ compounds.[22]

$$R_3SiCH_2CH_2OH + R'OH + R'OH_2{}^+ \longrightarrow$$
$$R_3SiOR' + CH_2{=}CH_2 + H_2O + R'OH_2{}^+ \qquad (8\text{-}25)$$

For $Me_3SiCH_2CH_2OH$, which had sufficient solubility in aqueous acid to be studied in that medium, the rate law involved dependence on the Hammett acidity function. Thus, a plot of log k vs. $-H_0$ was linear with a slope of unity for the following aqueous acids: H_2SO_4, $HClO_4$, HNO_3, and HCl. The rate law for (8-25) is as follows:[23]

[22] L. H. Sommer and R. A. Miller, unpublished work; see R. A. Miller, Ph.D. Thesis, The Pennsylvania State University, 1957.

[23] For the meaning of H_0 and its measurements, see L. P. Hammett, "Physical Organic Chemistry," McGraw-Hill Book Company, New York, 1940, pp. 267–277.

$$- \frac{d[\text{R}_3\text{SiCH}_2\text{CH}_2\text{OH}]}{dt} = k(h_0)[\text{R}_3\text{SiCH}_2\text{CH}_2\text{OH}]$$

$$H_0 = -\log h_0$$

Pertinent data for relative rates in 50 vol. % aqueous methanol with sulfuric acid are given in Table 8-9.

A Hammett reaction constant was calculated using the two arylsilanes and gave $\rho = -1.85$. Thus, electron-donating groups facilitate rate in reaction series (8-23) and (8-25).

Calculation of steric substituent constants assuming $\rho^* = \rho = -1.85$ gave: $E_s = -0.09$ for a single ethyl group, using data for compounds 1 and 2; $E_s = -0.11$ for a single ethyl group, using data for compounds 1 and 3, and then dividing ΣE_s by 2; $E_s = -0.10$ for a single ethyl group, using data for compounds 1 and 4, and then dividing ΣE_s by 3; $E_s = -0.31$ for a single isopropyl group.

It is interesting to summarize the available quantitative data on polar and steric effects of substituents for R_3SiX reactions and to compare these with corresponding data for organic reactions of known mechanism. This is done in Table 8-10.

Data for the reaction series (C-1), (C-2), (C-3), and (C-4) represent a wide range of mechanism for carbon. Series (C-1) and (C-2) involve an addition mechanism which is not possible for saturated carbon. Series (C-3) involves a direct displacement

Table 8-9

Structural effects on acid-catalyzed solvolysis rates of $\text{R}_3\text{SiCH}_2\text{CH}_2\text{OH}$ in 50% methanol at 25.0°

No.	R_3Si	k/k_0
1	Me_3Si	1.000^a
2	$(\text{C}_2\text{H}_5)\text{Me}_2\text{Si}$	1.24
3	$(\text{C}_2\text{H}_5)_2\text{MeSi}$	1.41
4	$(\text{C}_2\text{H}_5)_3\text{Si}$	1.76
5	$(i\text{-C}_3\text{H}_7)\text{Me}_2\text{Si}$	1.09
6	$(\text{C}_6\text{H}_5)\text{Me}_2\text{Si}$	0.089
7	$(m\text{-CF}_3\text{C}_6\text{H}_4)\text{Me}_2\text{Si}$	0.015

^{a} For $\text{Me}_3\text{SiCH}_2\text{CH}_2\text{OH}$, the first-order rate constant in 50% methanol containing 4.0 M sulfuric acid is $k_1 = 4.04 \times 10^{-3}$ sec.$^{-1}$.

Table 8-10
Polar and steric effects of substituents on rate

Reaction series	Reactant	Reaction	Catalyst	ρ or ρ^*	$E_s(C_2H_5)^a$	$E_s(i\text{-}C_3H_7)^a$	$E_s(t\text{-}C_4H_9)$
(8-1)	R_3SiH	Solvolysis	Base	$+4.30$	~ 0.00	-0.40	-1.87
(8-2)	R_3SiH	Chlorination	None	-4.20	~ 0.00	-0.42	
(8-5)	R_3SiH	Solvolysis	Acid	$+0.77$	~ 0.00	-0.34	
(8-6)	$R_3SiOMen$	Solvolysis	Base	$+2.70$	-0.78	-2.27	
(8-7)	$R_3SiOMen$	Solvolysis	Acid	-1.20	-0.72	-2.17	
(8-22)	R_3SiF	Solvolysis	Acid	$+0.82$		-0.72^b	
(8-23)	$R_3SiCH_2CH_2Cl$	Solvolysis	None	-2.15	-0.23	-0.59	
(8-25)	$R_3SiCH_2CH_2OH$	Solvolysis	Acid	-1.85	-0.10	-0.31	
(C-1)	$RCOOC_2H_5$	Hydrolysis	Base	$+2.48$	-0.07	-0.47	-1.54
(C-2)	$RCOOC_2H_5$	Hydrolysis	Acid	0.00	-0.07	-0.47	-1.54
(C-3)	RCH_2OTs	Solvolysis	None	-0.72			
(C-4)	$RR'R''CCl$	Solvolysis	None	-3.29			

^{a} E_s values for individual reaction series [except for (8-22)] are referred to methyl as a standard; i.e., $E_s \equiv 0.00$ for methyl.
^{b} The value for $E_s(i\text{-}C_3H_7)$ in series (8-22) is referred to ethyl as a standard.

(S_N2) mechanism. Series (C-4) involves an ionization (S_N1) mechanism. The four series cover a range in ρ^* from $+2.48$ to -3.29. This range is more than matched by data for R_3SiX series.

The known data for ionization reactions of tertiary organic chlorides indicate that steric hindrance is almost of no importance for (C-4). Indeed, examples of steric acceleration are known, resulting from relief of strain in the transition state relative to the reactant state. In this respect none of the R_3SiX series in Table 8-10 parallels (C-4).

8-3   Effects of the leaving group and the reagent

We have already noted the profound effects of substituents on rate, and we may begin the present discussion of leaving group and reagent effects by referring to three reaction series in which the leaving group was systematically varied while keeping the leaving atom the same. This is the simplest type of variation and the easiest to interpret quantitatively.

Two of the reaction series are similar to (8-20) and (8-21)

except that $R_3Si = (C_2H_5)_3Si$ in all the compounds studied, and structure variation was in the phenolate leaving group.

$$(C_2H_5)_3SiOC_6H_4X + ROH + RO^- \longrightarrow$$
$$(C_2H_5)_3SiOR + XC_6H_4O^- + ROH \qquad (8\text{-}26)$$

$$(C_2H_5)_3SiOC_6H_4X + ROH + ROH_2^+ \longrightarrow$$
$$(C_2H_5)_3SiOR' + XC_6H_4OH + R'OH_2^+ \qquad (8\text{-}27)$$

Table 8-11 gives representative data for meta and para substituents in the phenolate group.[24]

For series (8-26) the rate data are correlated by $\rho = +1.74$. For (8-27), $\rho = -0.533$. With regard to (8-26) it is interesting to note that the ionization constants for meta- and para-substituted phenols in water at 25° have $\rho = +2.01$. Thus, the effect on rate of the leaving group in (8-26) closely parallels its ability to bear a negative charge. In other words, a decrease in the pK_a of the conjugate acid of the leaving group brings about an increase in rate for reactions with basic reagents.

Compared to (8-26), the effect of X on (8-27) is in the opposite direction and is smaller. However, consideration of the probable gross mechanism[24] for the acid-catalyzed solvolyses indicates the reasons for the change in ρ.

[24] E. Akerman, *Acta Chem. Scand.*, **11**, 373 (1957).

Table 8-11
Solvolysis of $(C_2H_5)_3SiOC_6H_4X$

X	$k_{2(8\text{-}26)}$, l. mole^{-1} sec.$^{-1}$	$k_{2(8\text{-}27)}$, l. mole^{-1} sec.$^{-1}$	$\dfrac{k_{2(8\text{-}26)}}{k_{2(8\text{-}27)}}$
m-Cl	11.0	0.150	73
p-Cl	7.17	0.170	42
m-OMe	2.67	0.196	14
H	2.05	0.219	9.4
m-Me	1.43	0.244	5.9
p-OMe	1.22	0.396	3.1
p-Me	1.20	0.317	3.8
p-t-C$_4$H$_9$	1.19	0.290	4.1

$$(C_2H_5)_3SiOC_6H_4X + R\overset{+}{O}H_2 \underset{k_{-1}}{\overset{k_1}{\rightleftharpoons}}$$

$$(C_2H_5)_3Si\overset{+}{O}C_6H_4X + ROH \qquad (8\text{-}28)$$
$$H$$

$$ROH + (C_2H_5)_3Si\overset{+}{O}C_6H_4X \xrightarrow{k_2}$$
$$H$$
$$(C_2H_5)_3Si\overset{+}{O}R + XC_6H_4OH \qquad (8\text{-}29)$$
$$H$$

$$(C_2H_5)_3Si\overset{+}{O}R + ROH \underset{k_{-3}}{\overset{k_3}{\rightleftharpoons}} (C_2H_5)_3SiOR + R\overset{+}{O}H_2 \qquad (8\text{-}30)$$
$$H$$

On the reasonable assumption that the rate-controlling step is (8-29), the actual rate law would be

$$+\frac{d[(C_2H_5)_3SiOR]}{dt} = k_2[(C_2H_5)_3Si\overset{+}{O}C_6H_4X][ROH] \qquad (8\text{-}31)$$
$$H$$

and the concentration of the conjugate acid of the phenoxysilane would be controlled by equilibrium (8-28) if $k_{-1} \gg k_2$, according to

$$K = \frac{[(C_2H_5)_3Si\overset{+}{O}HC_6H_4X][ROH]}{[(C_2H_5)_3SiOC_6H_4X][ROH_2^+]} \qquad (8\text{-}32)$$

Now, from (8-31) and (8-32), it follows that

$$+\frac{d[(C_2H_5)_3SiOR]}{dt} = k_2K[(C_2H_5)_3SiOC_6H_4X][R\overset{+}{O}H_2] \quad (8\text{-}33)$$

and (8-33) shows that the experimentally determined rate constants for (8-27) listed in Table 8-11 are really k_2K, the product of k_2 for the rate-controlling step by the equilibrium constant for the fast equilibrium in (8-28). However, the effect of X on K cannot be estimated quantitatively, and so we cannot estimate the effect of X on k_2 in (8-29). All we can say is that electron-withdrawing substituents in the phenoxy leaving group should decrease K by making the oxygen less basic. Thus, of itself this latter effect will give a negative ρ.

Table 8-12
Base-catalyzed solvolysis of $Me_3SiCH_2C_6H_4X$

X	Relative rate	X	Relative rate
p-NO$_2$	18×10^5	p-Cl	14
p-CONH$_2$	63×10^2	p-Me$_3$Si	9.6
m-Cl	63	H	1.0
m-CONHPh	31	p-Me	0.2
p-Br	19	p-MeO	~ 0.02

In aqueous methanol containing 39 wt. % water, benzyl groups are cleaved from silicon:[25]

$$Me_3SiCH_2C_6H_4X + R'OH + R'O^- \longrightarrow$$
$$Me_3SiOR' + CH_3C_6H_4X + R'O^- \quad (8\text{-}34)$$

Relative rates compared to benzyltrimethylsilane as a standard are given in Table 8-12 for meta- and para-substituted benzyl-silanes at a temperature of 49.7°. The data of Table 8-12 indicate a very large susceptibility of rate to the nature of X. Indeed, for reaction series (8-34), $\rho = +4.88$. The magnitude of ρ for this series would appear to require a mechanism in which considerable breaking of the benzyl-silicon bond has occurred in the rate-controlling transition state. It is highly unlikely that the effects of X could be so large if the mechanism involved rate-controlling *formation* of an addition complex. The polar effect of X in $Me_3SiCH_2C_6H_4X$ on the polarity of the silicon atom will be decreased by a factor of about 3 owing to the presence of a methylene group,[6] and since the usual σ values for X were used to determine ρ, this would correspond to an actual ρ for such an addition mechanism of about $+15$. This is much too high a value. Indeed, in the case of the base-catalyzed hydrolysis of ethyl phenylacetates, $XC_6H_4CH_2CO_2Et$, $\rho = +0.91$, compared to $\rho = +2.50$ for the corresponding reaction of ethyl benzoates.

The ethyl-silicon bond in $C_2H_5SiMe_3$ is quite resistant to cleavage by strong bases under ordinary conditions. Also, tetra-alkylsilanes, R_4Si, without polar substituents give no reaction with alcohol-water media. The presence of a single *beta*-Cl

[25] C. Eaborn and S. H. Parker, *J. Chem. Soc.*, 126 (1955).

substituent brings about an enormous increase in reactivity. Indeed, in 70% ethanol the solvolysis rate for cleavage of the β-chloroethyl group from silicon is comparable to the solvolysis rate for cleavage of —Cl from carbon in *t*-butyl chloride. Thus, we see again the pronounced effect on rate of an increase in the ability of the leaving group to accept a negative charge (see Table 8-8):

$$\overset{\delta+}{\equiv}\!Si\!-\!-\!-\!C\!=\!=\!=\!C\!-\!-\!-\!\overset{\delta-}{Cl}$$

In reaction series (8-25) the presence of a single β-OH substituent again illustrates the same principle:

$$\overset{\delta+}{\equiv}\!Si\!-\!-\!-\!C\!=\!=\!=\!C\!-\!-\!-\!\overset{+}{O}H_2$$

This time the leaving group gives ethylene and water as the products of its decomposition. Reaction series (8-23) and (8-25) formally resemble the β-elimination reactions of organic halides and alcohols. But the participation of a β-silicon instead of a β-hydrogen can increase rate enormously.

We may conclude this section with three general observations which summarize structure-reactivity trends. However, they cannot be regarded as principles because of the pronounced polar and steric effects of substituents on the rates of many organosilicon reactions. Steric effects of the leaving group and steric requirements of the attacking reagent are other complicating factors.

1. In general, increased ability of the leaving group to accept a negative charge results in increased rates with nucleophilic reagents.

2. In general, ρ^* or ρ increases in the positive direction with an increase in the nucleophilicity of the attacking reagent.

3. In general, ρ^* or ρ changes in the negative direction with an increase in the electrophilicity of the attacking reagent.

8-4   Effects of the solvent

Unfortunately, systematic studies of solvent effects on the rates of R_3SiX reactions have been few in number. However, general observation and data discussed previously appear to indicate that the reaction rates of R_3SiX are generally increased with an increase in the polarity and ionizing power of the medium. This is to be expected on the basis of the Hughes-Ingold theory of solvent action when the attacking reagent is a neutral (uncharged) nucleophile, regardless of whether the mechanism is S_N2-Si or S_N1-Si, since both these mechanisms require charge separation at the rate-controlling transition state. For an S_N2-Si transition state involving water as the attacking nucleophile we would have approximately:

$$\overset{\delta+}{H_2O}\text{---}\overset{R_3}{Si}\text{---}\overset{\delta-}{X}$$

It is obvious that S_N1-Si which involves siliconium ion-pair formation will be facilitated by polar solvents.

Mechanism S_Ni-Si probably does not operate in polar solvents, and the effect of solvent variation on the rates of reactions proceeding by this mechanism is as yet largely unknown.

If the attacking nucleophile is a lyate ion derived from the solvent or a dissociated negative ion in general, Y^-, the effect of changing the polarity of the medium will not only involve a change in the rate constant k_2 for reaction of R_3SiX with Y^-, but will also affect the concentration of Y^-. In these circumstances, the effect of changing the polarity of the medium on the observed rate of reaction may be complex for cases in which the equilibrium-controlled concentration of Y^- is sensitive to the nature of the medium. Thus, although increased solvent polarity may tend to depress k_2 for an S_N2-Si reaction in which Y^- is the attacking nucleophile, the same change in solvent polarity may increase the concentration of Y^- and lead to increased reaction rates.

chapter **Bridgehead silicon**
nine

9-1 Introduction

The very elegant syntheses and studies of bridgehead organic halides (carbon at the bridgehead) by Bartlett and coworkers[1] have played a very important part in the elucidation of the stereochemical requirements for substitution at a saturated carbon atom, by S_N2 and S_N1 mechanisms, because of the special geometrical situation which exists at a bridgehead atom. This situation effectively prevents rearward attack and also greatly hinders formation of a planar carbonium ion, especially with bridgehead systems, such as the bicyclo[2,2,1]heptyl system, which have considerable angle strain. For such systems an S_N2 mechanism is evidently impossible for carbon, and S_N1 ionization reactions show greatly decreased rates.

Prior to the work with optically active organosilicon compounds, a start was made in the direction of clarifying the stereochemical requirements for substitution at a silicon atom by the synthesis and study of two bridgehead silicon systems.

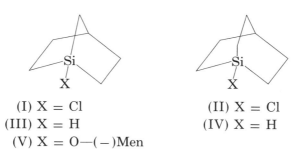

(I) X = Cl   (II) X = Cl
(III) X = H   (IV) X = H
(V) X = O—(−)Men

Compounds I, III, and V contain the 1-silabicyclo[2,2,1]heptyl system. Compounds II and IV contain the 1-silabicyclo[2,2,2]-octyl system.[2,3]

9-2 Bridgehead silicon chlorides

The bridgehead chloride (I) has an acrid odor, hydrolyzes rapidly in a stream of moist air to give the disiloxane, and undergoes

[1] P. D. Bartlett and L. H. Knox, *J. Am. Chem. Soc.,* **61,** 3184 (1939); P. D. Bartlett and E. S. Lewis, *ibid.,* **72,** 1005 (1950).

[2] L. H. Sommer and O. F. Bennett, *J. Am. Chem. Soc.,* **79,** 1008 (1957).

[3] L. H. Sommer and O. F. Bennett, *J. Am. Chem. Soc.,* **81,** 251 (1959).

rapid quantitative titration of its Si—Cl bond with 0.1 N alkali. Furthermore, I reacts very rapidly with lithium aluminum hydride in ether at 0° to give the Si—H compound (III). Qualitative observation indicates that bridgehead chloride (II) is less reactive than I, but II also undergoes rapid reduction with lithium aluminum hydride in ether at 0° and gives compound IV. Thus, in sharp contrast to their carbon analogues, bridgehead chlorides I and II are very reactive toward hydrolysis and lithium aluminum hydride reduction.

The present author suggests that, contrary to earlier hypotheses,[2,3] the rapid reactions of the Si—Cl bonds in I and II with water and lithium aluminum hydride pursue an S_N2-Si mechanism path which, in contrast to analogous acyclic R_3Si^*Cl reactions, proceeds with retention of configuration.

Construction of an accurately scaled model of the 1-silabicyclo[2,2,1]heptane system indicates that C—Si—C bond angles of the order of 90 to 100° permit the carbon atoms in the ring system to maintain tetrahedral angles. Thus, in I the carbon-silicon skeleton has the requisite geometry for retention already "built in" in the ground state. Direct displacement (part bonds to X and Y) requires no movement of R groups in I, in important contrast to S_N2-Si inversion and S_Ni-Si retention reactions of acyclic R_3Si^*X. In contrast to the lack of reactivity at analogous bridgehead carbon, $3d$ orbital participation and the relatively large size of silicon make possible the rapid attainment of the transition states shown in Fig. 9-1 for the special case of I.

In the case of II an accurately scaled model shows that the

Fig. 9-1   Two possible representations of an S_N2-Si transition state, giving retention of configuration.

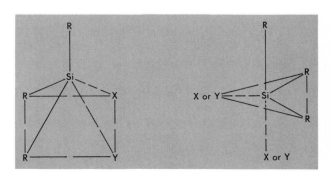

C—Si—C bond angles are somewhat smaller than the tetrahedral when the carbon atoms maintain their tetrahedral angles. But distortion of the bridgehead angles to give ~100° is easily possible and this would lead again to the possibility of S_N2-Si retention via a tetragonal pyramidal transition state. In any event, indications are that II is considerably less reactive than I.

In view of the preceding discussion, it is extremely interesting to note the report that 1,3,5,7-tetrachloro-1,3,5,7-tetrasilaadamantane is extremely resistant to hydrolysis and reaction with Grignard reagent.[4] Furthermore, it has been found that this substance requires more than a week for complete reduction of its silicon-chlorine bonds with lithium aluminum hydride.[5] The tetrasilaadamantane has four bridgehead silicon atoms whose angles are rigidly locked in the tetrahedral by the nature of the ring system which is (in contrast to I and II) *completely free from angle strain and from conformational strain.* The latter two factors are expected to strongly resist any distortion of the bridgehead angles from the tetrahedral. Thus, an S_N2-Si inversion mechanism cannot operate, and an S_N2-Si retention mechanism is opposed by the nature of the ring system. The result is that the bridgehead Si—Cl bonds in 1,3,5,7-tetrachloro-1,3,5,7-tetrasilaadamantane are very unreactive.

9-3   Bridgehead silicon hydrides

In the preceding section we have focused on geometrical factors connected with bridgehead ring systems, but examination of

[4] A. L. Smith and H. A. Clark, *J. Am. Chem. Soc.*, **83**, 3345 (1961).
[5] C. L. Frye, private communication.

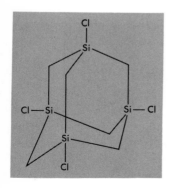

Fig. 9-2   1,3,5,7-Tetrachloro-1,3,5,7-tetrasilaadamantane.

Table 9-1
Infrared stretching frequency and proton magnetic resonance values for R_3SiH

Silane	I.R. SiH cm^{-1}	P. M. R. Shielding Values τ, p.p.m.
$(C_2H_5)_3SiH$	2097[a]	6.40[b]
II	2134[c]	6.13[c]
I	2148[c]	5.52[c]
$(C_2H_5)_2(Cl)SiH$	2153[a]	
$(CH_3)_2(Cl)SiH$		5.13[b]

[a] Taken from ref. 6.
[b] Taken from ref. 7.
[c] L. H. Sommer and N. C. Lloyd, unpublished work.

Table 9-1 will serve to indicate that the ground-state nature of the Si—H bond is also modified for bridgehead silicon.

From examination of Table 9-1 it is clear that the infrared stretching frequency for Si—H in I is significantly higher than for ordinary R_3SiH compounds and that the H is considerably less shielded in I. Both these changes also appear to be true for II, but to a much lesser extent.

Relative to acyclic compounds, angle strain in compounds I and II may be expected to result in increased p character of the ring silicon-carbon bonds. This would result in increased s character of the Si—X bonds in I and II. Smith[6] has correlated infrared Si—H stretching frequency values with electronegativity of the substituents on Si, and has concluded that increased frequency values reflect an increase in the s character of Si—H.

Table 9-1 shows that the effect on Si—H of placing the silicon at bridgehead positions in I and II is quite pronounced, and that the effect is directionally the same as placing a highly electronegative substituent (such as Cl) on silicon. We may call such an effect at strained bridgehead silicon an orbital-hybridization effect.

We turn next to the discussion of some relative rates data for bridgehead Si—H bonds.

For reactions of R_3SiH with OH^- in 95% ethanol at 35°

[6] A. L. Smith and N. C. Angelotti, *Spectrochim. Acta*, 412 (1959).
[7] D. E. Webster, *J. Chem. Soc.*, 5132 (1960).

[see series (8-1) in the preceding chapter], relative rates k_2 are, for $(C_2H_5)_3SiH = 1$: compound I, 10^3; compound II, 10^1 (ref. 8). Reaction series (8-1) has $\rho^* = +4.3$, indicating generation of considerable negative charge at silicon in the transition state. In this circumstance, I shows greatly enhanced rate and II moderately enhanced rate. Operation of favorable I-strain and orbital-hybridization factors is thus indicated. Mechanisms for I and II in these reactions are probably S_N2-Si with retention of configuration.

For reactions of R_3SiH with chlorine in carbon tetrachloride solvent [see reaction series (8-2) in the preceding chapter], relative rates k_2 are, for $(CH_3)_3SiH = 1$: compound I, 4×10^{-3}; compound II, 6×10^{-2}. Reaction series (8-2) has $\rho^* = -4.2$, indicating generation of significant positive charge at silicon in the transition state. In this circumstance, I shows greatly decreased reactivity and II moderately decreased rate.

Since chlorination of R_3Si^*H in carbon tetrachloride solvent proceeds with pure retention of configuration, the decreased rates for I and II in this series are extremely significant. They are probably due to the rate-depressing effect of the orbital-hybridization factor on reactions which place a considerable *positive charge* on silicon in the transition state. In a preceding chapter (Sec. 6-4) it was proposed that chlorination of R_3Si^*H involves formation of an intermediate in which the silicon must bear such a charge.

$$\left[R_3Si^*{\overset{\oplus}{\underset{Cl}{\overset{H}{\diagdown}}}} \right] \cdots Cl^\ominus$$

9-4   Chloride-chloride exchange at bridgehead silicon

In a previous chapter (Sec. 5-4) it was proposed that the mechanism of chloride-radiochloride exchange of R_3Si^*Cl with $C_6H_{11}NH_3Cl^{36}$ in chloroform solvent involves rate-controlling formation of a siliconium ion-pair.

---

[8] L. H. Sommer, O. F. Bennett, P. G. Campbell, and D. R. Weyenberg, *J. Am. Chem. Soc.*, **79**, 3295 (1957); and ref. 3.

$$[R_3Si^*]^{\oplus} \cdots [Cl]^{\ominus}$$

If this hypothesis is correct, we would expect, on the basis of the preceding section, that the rate of chloride-chloride exchange at bridgehead silicon in compound I should be much *less* than for $(C_2H_5)_3SiCl$. It was found[9] that this is so; for $(C_2H_5)_3SiCl = 1$, compound I had $k_{(ex.)} = 2 \times 10^{-3}$.

[9] L. H. Sommer and F. O. Stark, unpublished work.

chapter *ten* **Recent advances**

10-1 New optically active systems

Previous chapters have dealt with the stereochemistry of asymmetric silicon in α-naphthylphenylmethylsilanes. Recently[1] other optically active organosilicon systems have become available, and this section presents a brief summary of the synthesis, stereochemistry, and absolute configurations of these new systems.

The synthetic route to the new systems makes use of optically active α-NpPhMeSi*Cl and an organolithium compound, RLi, for conversion to α-NpPhMeSi*R. Reaction of the latter with bromine gives α-bromonaphthalene and PhMeRSi*Br, which is then converted to PhMeRSi*H by lithium aluminum hydride reduction. Purification of the new system, removal of α-bromonaphthalene and small amounts of other organic products, is best accomplished after reduction.

$$\alpha\text{-NpPhMeSi*Cl} \xrightarrow{\text{RLi}} \alpha\text{-NpPhMeSi*R} \qquad (10\text{-}1)$$

$$\alpha\text{-NpPhMeSi*R} \xrightarrow{\text{Br}_2} \text{PhMeSi*Br} \qquad (10\text{-}2)$$

$$\text{PhMeSi*Br} \xrightarrow{\text{LiAlH}_4} \text{PhMeSi*H} \qquad (10\text{-}3)$$

By the above synthetic procedure three new optically active systems have been synthesized, in which R is neopentyl, benzhydryl, and ethyl. All three give highly stereospecific Walden cycles which parallel completely those observed for the α-naphthylphenylmethylsilyl system, e.g.:

$$(+)\text{neoC}_5\text{H}_{11}\text{PhMeSi*H} \xrightarrow[\text{Ret.}]{\text{Cl}_2}$$
$$[\alpha]_D +2.5°$$
$$\qquad (+)\text{neoC}_5\text{H}_{11}\text{PhMeSi*Cl} \xrightarrow[\text{Inv.}]{\text{LiAlH}_4}$$
$$\qquad [\alpha]_D +5.9°$$
$$\qquad\qquad (-)\text{neoC}_5\text{H}_{11}\text{PhMeSi*H} \qquad (10\text{-}4)$$
$$\qquad\qquad [\alpha]_D -2.5°$$

$$(+)\text{Ph}_2\text{CHPhMeSi*H} \xrightarrow[\text{Ret.}]{\text{Cl}_2} (+)\text{Ph}_2\text{CHPhMeSi*Cl} \xrightarrow[\text{Inv.}]{\text{LiAlH}_4}$$
$$[\alpha]_D +7.1° \qquad\qquad [\alpha]_D +14.1°$$
$$\qquad\qquad (-)\text{Ph}_2\text{CHPhMeSi*Cl} \qquad (10\text{-}5)$$
$$\qquad\qquad [\alpha]_D -6.4°$$

[1] L. H. Sommer, K. W. Michael, and W. D. Korte, *J. Am. Chem. Soc.*, **85,** 3712 (1963).

$$(+)\text{EtPhMeSi*H} \xrightarrow[\text{Ret.}]{\text{Cl}_2} (+)\text{EtPhMeSi*Cl} \xrightarrow[\text{Inv.}]{\text{LiAlH}_4}$$
$$[\alpha]_D +1.7° \qquad\qquad [\alpha]_D +2.0°$$
$$(-)\text{EtPhMeSi*H} \qquad (10\text{-}6)$$
$$[\alpha]_D -1.7°$$

Bromination to $\equiv$Si*Br and lithium aluminum hydride reduction to $\equiv$Si*H give parallel results. *In these, and in every other stereochemical reaction thus far investigated with the new systems, stereochemistry for the new systems is the same as for the α-naphthylphenylmethylsilyl system.* Tables 10-1, 10-2, and 10-3 give the stereochemical results obtained thus far.

Table 10-1
Summary of stereochemistry and mechanism for neopentylphenylmethylsilanes, neoC$_5$H$_{11}$PhMeSi*X

R$_3$Si*X reactant	Reagent	Solvent	Product	Stereo-chemistry	Mechanism
(+)SiOH	LiAlH$_4$	Bu$_2$O	(+)SiH	Ret.	S$_N$i-Si
(+)SiOMe	LiAlH$_4$	Ether	(+)SiH	Ret.	S$_N$i-Si
(+)SiOMe	KOH(s)	Xylene	(+)SiOH^a	Ret.	S$_N$i-Si
(+)SiOCOCH$_3$	LiAlH$_4$	Ether	(−)SiH	Inv.	S$_N$2-Si
(+)SiOCOCH$_3$	KOH(s)	Xylene	(−)SiOH^a	Inv.	S$_N$2-Si
(+)SiOCOCH$_3$	MeOH	Pentane^b	(−)SiOMe	Inv.	S$_N$2-Si
(+)SiCl	H$_2$O	Ether	(−)SiOH	Inv.	S$_N$2-Si
(+)SiCl	MeOH	Pentane^b	(−)SiOMe	Inv.	S$_N$2-Si
(+)SiCl	NaB(OMe)$_4$	Ether	(−)SiOMe	Inv.	S$_N$2-Si
(+)SiCl	Hg(OCOMe)$_2$	C$_6$H$_6$	(−)SiOCOCH$_3$	Inv.	S$_N$2-Si
(+)SiCl	LiAlH$_4$	Ether	(−)SiH	Inv.	S$_N$2-Si
(+)SiCl	α-NpLi	Ether	(−)Si-α-Np	Inv.	S$_N$2-Si
(+)SiCl	cycloC$_6$H$_{11}$NH$_3$F	CHCl$_3$	(−)SiF	Inv.	S$_N$2-Si
(+)SiBr	H$_2$O	Ether	(−)SiOH	Inv.	S$_N$2-Si
(+)SiBr	MeOH	Pentane^b	(−)SiOMe	Inv.	S$_N$2-Si
(+)SiBr	LiAlH$_4$	Ether	(−)SiH	Inv.	S$_N$2-Si
(+)SiBr	cycloC$_6$H$_{11}$NH$_3$Cl	CHCl$_3$	(−)SiCl	Inv.	S$_N$2-Si
(+)SiBr	cycloC$_6$H$_{11}$NH$_3$F	CHCl$_3$	(−)SiF	Inv.	S$_N$2-Si
(+)SiCl		CH$_3$NO$_2$	(±)SiCl	Rac.	S$_N$1-Si
(+)SiH	Cl$_2$	CCl$_4$	(+)SiCl	Ret.	(S$_N$i-S$_E$i)-Si
(+)SiH	Br$_2$	CCl$_4$	(+)SiBr	Ret.	(S$_N$i-S$_E$i)-Si
(+)SiH	KOH(s)	Xylene	(+)SiOH^a	Ret.	S$_N$i-Si
(+)Si-α-Np	Br$_2$	Benzene	(−)SiBr	Inv.	S$_N$2-Si

^{a} The product from reaction with KOH(s) is R$_3$Si*OK, which is converted to R$_3$Si*OH by hydrolysis.
^{b} Cyclohexylamine was used as an acid acceptor.

Table 10-2

Summary of stereochemistry and mechanism for benzhydrylphenylmethylsilanes, $Ph_2CHPhMeSi*X$

R_3Si*X reactant	Reagent	Solvent	Product	Stereochemistry	Mechanism
$(+)SiOMe$	$LiAlH_4$	Ether	$(+)SiH$	Ret.	S_Ni-Si
$(+)SiOH$	$LiAlH_4$	Et_2O-Bu_2O	$(+)SiH$	Ret.	S_Ni-Si
$(+)SiO$-cyclo-C_6H_{11}	$LiAlH_4$	Et_2O-Bu_2O	$(+)SiH$	Ret.	S_Ni-Si
$(-)SiOCOCH_3$	$LiAlH_4$	Ether	$(-)SiH$	Inv.	S_N2-Si
$(-)SiOCOCH_3$	$MeOH$	Pentane[a]	$(-)SiOMe$	Inv.	S_N2-Si
$(+)SiCl$	H_2O	Ether	$(-)SiOH$	Inv.	S_N2-Si
$(+)SiCl$	$MeOH$	Pentane[a]	$(-)SiOMe$	Inv.	S_N2-Si
$(+)SiCl$	$NaB(OMe)_4$	Ether	$(-)SiOMe$	Inv.	S_N2-Si
$(+)SiCl$	$LiAlH_4$	Ether	$(-)SiH$	Inv.	S_N2-Si
$(+)SiCl$	cyclo$C_6H_{11}OH$	Pentane[a]	$(-)SiO$-cyclo-C_6H_{11}	Inv.	S_N2-Si
$(+)SiCl$	$KOCOCH_3$	Benzene	$(+)SiOCOCH_3$	Inv.	S_N2-Si
$(+)SiCl$	$Hg(OCOCH_3)_2$	Benzene	$(+)SiOCOCH_3$	Inv.	S_N2-Si
$(+)SiCl$	cyclo$C_6H_{11}NH_3F$	$CHCl_3$	$(-)SiF$	Inv.	S_N2-Si
$(+)SiBr$	H_2O	Ether	$(-)SiOH$	Inv.	S_N2-Si
$(+)SiBr$	$MeOH$	Pentane[a]	$(-)SiOMe$	Inv.	S_N2-Si
$(+)SiBr$	$LiAlH_4$	Ether	$(-)SiH$	Inv.	S_N2-Si
$(+)SiBr$	cyclo$C_6H_{11}NH_3F$	$CHCl_3$	$(-)SiF$	Inv.	S_N2-Si
$(+)SiH$	Cl_2	CCl_4	$(+)SiCl$	Ret.	$(S_Ni$-$S_Ei)$-Si
$(+)SiH$	Br_2	CCl_4	$(+)SiBr$	Ret.	$(S_Ni$-$S_Ei)$-Si
$(+)SiF$	$LiAlH_4$	Ether	$(-)SiH$	Inv.	S_N2-Si
$(+)Si$-α-Np	Br_2	Benzene	$(-)SiBr$	Inv.	S_N2-Si
$(+)SiCl$	α-NpLi	Ether	$(-)Si$-α-Np	Inv.	S_N2-Si
$(+)SiF$	α-NpLi	Ether	$(+)Si$-α-Np	Ret.	S_Ni-Si
$(+)SiCl$	EtLi	Ether	$(-)SiEt$	Inv.	S_N2-Si
$(+)SiF$	EtLi	Ether	$(+)SiEt$	Ret.	S_Ni-Si

[a] Cyclohexylamine was used as an acceptor for HX.

Relative configurations of the compounds within individual families of the new optically active systems have been obtained by chemical correlations of configuration for $\equiv Si*$—O— compounds, by experiments and arguments similar to those already discussed for the α-naphthylphenylmethylsilyl system, and also by analogy with the stereochemistry of corresponding reactions of the α-naphthylphenylmethylsilyl system. The result, complete internal consistency of stereochemical results for each system and complete parallelism of stereochemistry of reaction for all four systems, would be highly improbable if incorrect assignments of relative configuration had been made.

For each of the new systems, conversion of α-NpPhMeSi*R to its enantiomer takes place via a four-step Walden cycle in which bromine cleavage of the α-naphthyl group is assigned an inversion stereochemistry (I and II are enantiomers).

$$\alpha\text{-NpPhMeSi*R} \xrightarrow[\text{Inv.}]{\text{Br}_2} \text{PhMeRSi*Br} \xrightarrow[\text{Inv.}]{\text{LiAlH}_4}$$
$$\text{I}$$

$$\text{PhMeRSi*H} \xrightarrow[\text{Ret.}]{\text{Cl}_2} \text{PhMeRSi*Cl} \xrightarrow[\text{Inv.}]{\alpha\text{-NpLi}} \alpha\text{-NpPhMeSi*R}$$
$$\text{II}$$

The bromine cleavage of the p-methoxyphenyl group from α-NpPhMeSi*—C_6H_4-p-OMe has been assigned an inversion stereochemistry on sound grounds,[2] and assignment of an inversion stereochemistry for the bromine cleavage of α-naphthyl is in accord with that finding, and also with assignment of stereochemistry (based on analogous reactions of α-NpPhMeSi— compounds) for the other three steps in the above four-step Walden cycles.

The inversion stereochemistry for bromine cleavage of α-naphthyl establishes a configuration "bridge" between the new and the original optically active systems, and permits assignment of absolute configurations to compounds of the new systems —because of x-ray determination of absolute configuration for compounds of the original system. This is done below for the

[2] C. Eaborn and O. W. Steward, *Proc. Chem. Soc.*, 59 (1963).

Table 10-3
Summary of stereochemistry and mechanism for phenylethylmethylsilanes, PhEtMeSi*X

R_3Si*X reactant	Reagent	Solvent	Product	Stereo-chemistry	Mechanism
(+)SiCl	LiAlH$_4$	Ether	(−)SiH	Inv.	S_N2-Si
(+)SiBr	LiAlH$_4$	Ether	(−)SiH	Inv.	S_N2-Si
(+)SiCl	α-NpLi	Ether	(+)Si-α-Np	Inv.	S_N2-Si
(+)SiH	Cl$_2$	CCl$_4$	(+)SiCl	Ret.	(S_Ni-S_Ei)-Si
(−)Si-α-Np	Br$_2$	Benzene	(−)SiBr	Inv.	S_N2-Si

dextrorotatory $\equiv$Si*H compounds. The absolute configurations of the carbon analogues of phenylethylmethylsilane[3] and α-naphthylphenylmethylsilane[4] are included for comparison.

$$\alpha\text{-Np}\!\!-\!\!\underset{\underset{\displaystyle H}{|}}{\overset{\overset{\displaystyle Ph}{|}}{Si}}\!\!-\!\!Me$$

$[\alpha]_D +33°$

$$Ph_2CH\!\!-\!\!\underset{\underset{\displaystyle H}{|}}{\overset{\overset{\displaystyle Ph}{|}}{Si}}\!\!-\!\!Me$$

$[\alpha]_D +7.1°$

$$neoC_5H_{11}\!\!-\!\!\underset{\underset{\displaystyle H}{|}}{\overset{\overset{\displaystyle Ph}{|}}{Si}}\!\!-\!\!Me$$

$[\alpha]_D +2.5°$

$$Et\!\!-\!\!\underset{\underset{\displaystyle H}{|}}{\overset{\overset{\displaystyle Ph}{|}}{Si}}\!\!-\!\!Me$$

$[\alpha]_D +1.7°$

$$Et\!\!-\!\!\underset{\underset{\displaystyle H}{|}}{\overset{\overset{\displaystyle Ph}{|}}{C}}\!\!-\!\!Me$$

$[\alpha]_D +24°$, neat, 1 dm.

$$\alpha\text{-Np}\!\!-\!\!\underset{\underset{\displaystyle H}{|}}{\overset{\overset{\displaystyle Ph}{|}}{C}}\!\!-\!\!Me$$

$[\alpha]_D +7.5°$

Tables 10-4, 10-5, and 10-6 give absolute configurations for optically active compounds in the three new series.

10-2   Coupling reactions with organometallic reagents: significance for mechanism

During the time of writing of the first nine chapters of this book stereochemical data concerning coupling reactions of asymmetric silicon with organometallic reagents have been greatly increased. Data for coupling reactions of α-naphthylphenylmethylsilanes, α-NpPhMeSi*X, are summarized in Table 10-7 because of their considerable significance for mechanism clarification.

Reactions of α-NpPhMeSi*Cl with R'Li proceed in excellent

[3] D. J. Cram and J. Allinger, *J. Am. Chem. Soc.,* **76,** 4518 (1954).
[4] A. G. Brook, *J. Am. Chem. Soc.,* **85,** 3051 (1963).

Table 10-4
neoC$_5$H$_{11}$PhMeSi*X compounds having the configuration

$$neoC_5H_{11}\!-\!\underset{\underset{X}{|}}{\overset{\overset{Ph}{|}}{Si}}\!-\!Me$$

Si*X	$[\alpha]_D$, solvent
(+)SiH	+2.5°, CCl$_4$
(+)SiF	+5.0°, pentane
(+)SiCl	+7.5°, CCl$_4$
(+)SiBr	+10.1°, CCl$_4$
(+)SiOH	+7.5°, pentane
(+)SiOMe	+13.7°, pentane
(+)SiOCOCH$_3$	+2.2°, pentane
(+)Si-α-Np	+23.2°, pentane

yield and invariably give α-NpPhMeSi*R with inversion of configuration. Furthermore, many of these reactions are highly stereospecific.

Table 10-5
Ph$_2$CHPhMeSi*X compounds having the configuration

$$Ph_2CH\!-\!\underset{\underset{X}{|}}{\overset{\overset{Ph}{|}}{Si}}\!-\!Me$$

Si*X	$[\alpha]_D$, solvent	m. p.
(+)SiH	+7.1°, chloroform	57°
(+)SiF	+11.6°, pentane	81°
(+)SiCl	+14.1°, ether	68°
(+)SiBr	+16.3°, pentane	
(+)SiOH	+17.9°, pentane	
(+)SiOMe	+27.1°, pentane	
(+)SiO-cycloC$_6$H$_{11}$	+25.2°, pentane	
(−)SiOCOCH$_3$	−6.7°, pentane	
(+)SiEt	+11.9°, pentane	
(+)Si-α-Np	+17.1°, chloroform	

Table 10-6
EtPhMeSi*X compounds having the configuration

$$\begin{array}{c} Ph \\ | \\ Et \!\!\blacktriangleright\!\! Si \!\!\blacktriangleleft\!\! Me \\ | \\ X \end{array}$$

Si*X	$[\alpha]_D$, solvent
(+)SiH	+1.7°, CCl_4
(+)SiCl	+2.0°, CCl_4
(+)SiBr	+2.3°, benzene
(−)Si-α-Np	−6.2°, pentane

These findings effectively dispose of possible operation of an S_N2^*-Si mechanism for which $k_{-1} \gg k_2$ would obtain in the following formulation:

$$R'Li + \alpha\text{-NpPhMeSi}^*Cl \underset{k_{-1}}{\overset{k_1}{\rightleftharpoons}} \begin{bmatrix} Me & \overset{\displaystyle Ph}{\underset{\displaystyle |}{}} & \alpha\text{-Np} \\ & Si & \\ Cl & & R' \end{bmatrix}^{\ominus} Li^{\oplus}$$

$$\begin{bmatrix} Me & \overset{\displaystyle Ph}{\underset{\displaystyle |}{}} & \alpha\text{-Np} \\ & Si & \\ Cl & & R' \end{bmatrix}^{\ominus} Li^{\oplus} \xrightarrow{k_2} \alpha\text{-NpPhMeSi}^*R' + LiCl$$

It seems entirely unreasonable to expect that a full-fledged pentacovalent silicon intermediate (four organic groups bonded to silicon by equally full bonds and one full bond to Cl) could return many times to R'Li and R_3Si^*Cl with (1) pure retention of configuration, and (2) without any exchange of organic groups.

Operation of an S_N2^{**}-Si mechanism, for which formation of the intermediate is slow (k_1) and rate-controlling and $k_2 \gg k_{-1}$, is also improbable for R_3Si^*Cl plus R'Li. Previous discussion clearly shows that the ability of a leaving group to stabilize a negative charge is a critical factor in stereochemistry and mechanism. This strongly implies that all the reactions of R_3SiCl involve stretching of the Si—Cl bond in the rate-controlling transition state. The latter is inconsistent with operation of mechanism S_N2^{**}-Si for the reactions of R_3Si^*Cl. Thus, as

indicated in Table 10-7, the inversion reactions of R_3Si^*Cl with
$R'Li$ use an S_N2-Si mechanism.

The retention reactions of R_3Si^*H with $R'Li$ that are listed
in Table 10-7 cannot involve an S_N2^*-Si mechanism. For reasons

Table 10-7
Stereochemistry of coupling reactions of α-naphthylphenylmethylsilanes, α-NpPhMeSi*X, with organometallic reagents

R_3Si^*X reactant	Reagent	Solvent	Product	Stereo-chemistry	Mechanism
(+)SiCl	EtLi	Ether	(+)SiEt	Inv.	S_N2-Si
(−)SiF	EtLi	Ether	(−)SiEt	Ret.	S_Ni-Si
(+)SiCl	EtLi	Pentane	(+)SiEt	Inv.	S_N2-Si
(−)SiF	EtLi	Pentane	(−)SiEt	Ret.	S_Ni-Si
(+)SiCl	n-PrLi	Ether	(+)Si-n-Pr	Inv.	S_N2-Si
(−)SiF	n-PrLi	Ether	(−)Si-n-Pr	Ret.	S_Ni-Si
(+)SiH	n-PrLi	Pentane	(+)Si-n-Pr	Ret.	S_Ni-Si
(+)SiCl	iso-PrLi	Pentane[a]	(+)Si-iso-Pr	Inv.	S_N2-Si
(−)SiF	iso-PrLi	Pentane[a]	(−)Si-iso-Pr	Ret.	S_Ni-Si
(+)SiCl	n-BuLi	Ether	(−)Si-n-Bu	Inv.	S_N2-Si
(−)SiF	n-BuLi	Ether	(+)Si-n-Bu	Ret.	S_Ni-Si
(+)SiH	n-BuLi	Ether	(−)Si-n-Bu	Ret.	S_Ni-Si
(+)SiH	n-BuLi	Pentane	(−)Si-n-Bu	Ret.	S_Ni-Si
(+)SiCl	iso-BuLi	Ether	(−)Si-iso-Bu	Inv.	S_N2-Si
(−)SiF	iso-BuLi	Ether	(+)Si-iso-Bu	Ret.	S_Ni-Si
(+)SiCl	NeopentylLi	Ether	(−)Si-neopentyl	Inv.	S_N2-Si
(−)SiF	NeopentylLi	Ether	(+)Si-neopentyl	Ret.	S_Ni-Si
(+)SiCl	Ph₂CHLi	Ether	(−)Si-CHPh₂	Inv.	S_N2-Si
(−)SiF	Ph₂CHLi	Ether	(−)Si-CHPh₂	Inv.	S_N2-Si

[a] Reactions in ether gave racemic Si-i-Pr; slow reaction and faster racemization of Si—X by formed LiX in ether are probably responsible.

already given, such a mechanism would probably lead to extensive racemization and some exchange of organic groups. Neither of these is observed.

An S_N2^{**}-Si mechanism for the retention reactions of R_3Si^*H with $R'Li$ also seems improbable to this author. Such a mechanism would demand an intermediate containing four equally full bonds from silicon to the four organic groups and one full bond to H, and would not permit four-center character in the rate-controlling transition state. In the absence of the latter, it is difficult to discern any special driving force for retention of configuration. Certainly, nonbonded repulsions and interactions in the following structures of intermediates (R' is the entering group) which would lead to inversion and retention of configuration would be very similar.

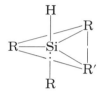

Retention intermediate   Inversion intermediate
for S_N2^{**}-Si   for S_N2^{**}-Si

As indicated in Table 10-7, the most likely mechanism for the retention reactions of $R'Li$ with R_3Si^*H is S_Ni-Si.

$$R_3Si^* \overset{H}{\underset{R'}{\diamond}} Li$$

The arrangement of the R groups with respect to Si is pyramidal, and overall geometry may be either tetragonal pyramid or trigonal bipyramid (see Figs. 3-3 and 3-4).

The above arguments in favor of an S_Ni-Si mechanism for R_3Si^*H and $R'Li$ may also be applied to the retention reactions of R_3Si^*F in Table 10-7.

$$R_3Si^* \overset{F}{\underset{R'}{\diamond}} Li$$

It is interesting to note the change in stereochemistry, from retention to inversion of configuration, when benzhydryllithium is used with R_3Si*F. In contrast to the carbon-lithium bonds of the simple alkyllithium reagents which give retention of configuration with R_3Si*F, benzhydryllithium is extensively ionized in ether solvent.[5] The change in mechanism from S_Ni-Si to S_N2-Si may be rationalized on the ground that operation of an S_Ni-Si mechanism is no longer required for assisting ionization of the carbon-lithium bond.[6]

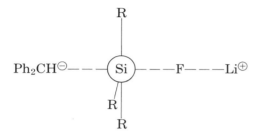

[5] *Cf.* V. R. Sandel and H. H. Friedman, *J. Am. Chem. Soc.,* **85,** 2329 (1963); R. Waack and M. A. Doran, *ibid.,* 4042.

[6] Many organolithium compounds are known to exist in solution as aggregates containing two or more RLi molecules, but this fact does not change the major mechanism implications of the above formulations.

**A general survey
of the stereochemistry
and mechanisms
of silicon centers**

11-1   Introduction

It seems desirable to provide a general survey and summary of the basic concepts and facts discussed in previous chapters.

11-2   Reaction profiles for S_N2-Si and S_Ni-Si mechanisms

It has been concluded that the reaction profiles shown in Figs. 11-1 and 11-2 are the most probable for most of the stereospecific reactions of R_3Si^*X.

For simplicity, Figs. 11-1 and 11-2 are drawn to represent reactions that are neither exothermic nor endothermic. But they are intended to apply generally.

In Fig. 11-2 the U.I. free-energy valley, corresponding to formation of an unstable intermediate, is flanked by maxima of approximately equal heights. Furthermore, Fig. 11-2 is intended to convey the postulate (for S_N2-Si and S_Ni-Si) that the structure and free energy of U.I. and the structures and free energies of the two transition-state maxima which precede and follow it in Fig. 11-2 are closely similar.

Fig. 11-1   **Reaction profile for a direct-displacement S_N2-Si or S_Ni-Si mechanism operating without involvement of an unstable intermediate.**

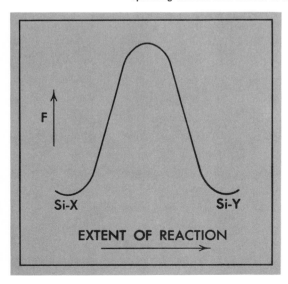

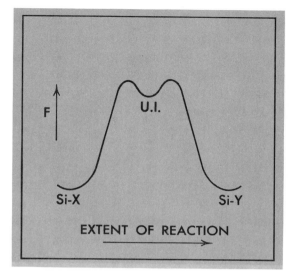

Fig. 11-2   Reaction profile for an S_N2-Si or S_Ni-Si mechanism involving an unstable intermediate.

11-3   The S_N2-Si mechanism

This is the most common mechanism for polar reactions of R_3SiX. *In acylic cases, inversion of configuration is the rule for operation of mechanism* S_N2-Si.

In the special case of bridgehead silicon which has the R—Si—R angles constrained below the tetrahedral value to ca. 90 to 100°, rapid reaction by mechanism S_N2-Si can proceed with retention of configuration. This is one difference between S_N2-Si and S_N2 for carbon. Another difference is possible participation of the $3d_{z^2}$ or $3d_{x^2-y^2}$ orbital when such participation can lower the free energy of the transition state in Fig. 11-1 or the free energy of U.I. and the transition state maxima in Fig. 11-2.

It must be emphasized that $3d$ orbital participation will occur *only* when it lowers the free energy of activation ($\Delta F^{\ddagger}$) for reaction, and that *participation of a 3d orbital does not require formation of an intermediate*.

Still another important difference between S_N2-Si for silicon and S_N2 for saturated carbon lies in the effect of $3d$ orbital participation on the polar effects of substituents on reaction rate.

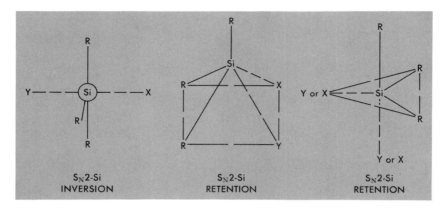

Fig. 11-3   Representation of S_N2-Si mechanisms.

Such participation can make transition-state silicon quite electron-rich (in some cases) relative to ground-state silicon. From a practical quantitative standpoint ρ or ρ^* can be large and positive for silicon, ca. $+3$, whereas ρ or ρ^* is of the order of $+0.8$ for S_N2 reactions of saturated carbon.

The similarity between S_N2 for saturated carbon and S_N2-Si for silicon lies in predominant inversion of configuration for both, via the trigonal bipyramid geometry shown in Fig. 11-3, and in the gross difference between the "bonds" to X and Y and those to the nonreacting groups. The former are long and weak relative to the latter.

Participation of silicon's $3d$ orbitals can lower the free energy of S_N2-Si transition states. This is one factor which contributes to the speed of S_N2-Si reactions. Another factor of great importance is undoubtedly the large size of silicon, covalent radius 1.17 Å., compared to carbon, covalent radius 0.77 Å. Still another factor is probably the greater polarizability of Si—X relative to C—X. The present author believes that the polarizability factor (see Table 1-8) is very significant for reactions of Si—X in general.

11-4   The S_Ni-Si mechanism

This is probably the most common retention mechanism for organosilicon reactions.   It is a mechanism which involves quasi-cyclic rate-controlling transition states which are generally four-center but may also be three-center:

Unlike the S_Ni mechanism for carbon, which generally involves ion-pair formation, the S_Ni-Si mechanism operates without siliconium ion-pair formation in many cases involving attack by strong nucleophilic reagents. Another difference between S_Ni-Si and S_Ni for carbon is the possible participation of silicon's $3d$ orbitals which permits the four-center structures in Fig. 11-4 to be either transition states (Fig. 11-1) or unstable intermediates (Fig. 11-2).

Although participation of silicon's $3d$ orbitals can lower the free energy of S_Ni-Si transition states for reactions with strong nucleophiles, the large size of silicon makes such reactions possible and common. Simple calculation shows that mechanism S_Ni-Si can operate without prohibitive nonbonded R - - - R repulsions in the structures shown in Fig. 11-4. Thus, the R - - - R distance for two R groups bonded to tetrahedral carbon (2.52 Å.) is smaller than the R - - - R distance for two R groups which make a 100° angle with Si (2.98 Å.), or even a 90° angle with Si (2.74 Å.). These values are for the distance between the terminal carbon atoms in different R groups.

If —X is a poor leaving group whose capacity to stabilize a negative charge is low (pK_a of HX larger than ca. 10), then

Fig. 11-4   Representation of S_Ni-Si mechanisms.

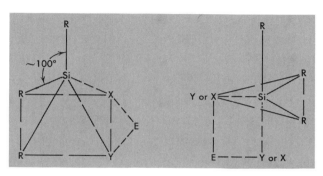

reactions of R_3Si^*X in solvents of poor ionizing power will often proceed by mechanism S_Ni-Si. The four-center character of S_Ni-Si mechanisms provides the necessary electrophilic assistance (by providing "pull" on the leaving group) and minimization of charge separation needed for removal of poor leaving groups in nonpolar solvents.

The geometry of reagent attack at the silicon tetrahedron for mechanism S_Ni-Si would be "broadside" to the Si—X bond for tetragonal pyramid geometry; "front-face" for trigonal bipyramid geometry in which Y is apical; and "front-edge" for trigonal bipyramid geometry in which Y is equatorial. In the absence of experimental data which can differentiate between these possibilities, the general term "frontside attack" would appear to be most appropriate for mechanism S_Ni-Si.

11-5   The S_N1-Si ionization mechanism

Reaction of R_3Si^*X by a siliconium ion-pair mechanism, termed S_N1-Si in this book, is less common than reaction by S_N2-Si and S_Ni-Si mechanisms. Nevertheless, this is a relative matter, and rapid rates for S_N1-Si reactions obtain under conditions favorable to its operation and unfavorable to operation of S_N2-Si and S_Ni-Si mechanisms (see below).

Operation of mechanism S_N1-Si is revealed by the evidence for "ion-pair return" in the solvent-induced racemization of R_3Si^*Cl in nitromethane-chloroform solvents.

In chloroform solvent, salt-induced ionization of R_3Si^*Cl to an ion-pair occurs when the anionic component of the salt is less basic and less nucleophilic (for Si) than —Cl. Under these circumstances racemization takes place without macroscopic displacement of —Cl. However, the S_N1-Si mechanism is unable to compete with operation of S_N2-Si when the anionic component of the salt is more basic and more nucleophilic (for Si) than is —Cl.

In chloroform solvent, the chloride-radiochloride exchange reaction of R_3Si^*Cl with cyclo$C_6H_{11}NH_3Cl^{36}$ gives $k_{(rac.)}/k_{(ex.)} = 1 \pm 0.1$. Rate-controlling salt-induced ionization of R_3Si^*Cl to an ion-pair followed by fast nonstereospecific chloride-chloride exchange with salt is consistent with the observed facts for

R_3Si^*Cl and also explains greatly decreased rate of chloride-chloride exchange at bridgehead silicon in 1-chloro-1-silabicyclo-[2,2,1]heptane.

Under other conditions more favorable to operation of an S_N2-Si mechanism, chloride-radiochloride exchange may not follow an S_N1-Si mechanism.

11-6 The S_N2^*-Si mechanism

This is a relatively rare mechanism for R_3SiX compounds. It has only been observed for R_3Si^*F in one case [racemization of R_3Si^*F by expanded-octet (EO) return]. But it is not even universal for R_3Si^*F in which the high bond energy of Si—F (ca. 130 kcal./mole) and high electronegativity of —F should be very favorable for operation of this mechanism. This mechanism is defined as involving formation of a full-fledged pentacovalent silicon intermediate, *five full bonds to central Si,* in a rapid equilibrium step, followed by rate-controlling conversion of the intermediate to products. The attacking reagent Y is a nucleophile.

In the following kinetic formulation for mechanism S_N2^*-Si, $k_{-1} \gg k_2$, $k_{-1} \gg k_1$, and the intermediate is unstable and conforms to the steady-state approximation:

$$R_3Si^*X + Y \underset{k_{-1}}{\overset{k_1}{\rightleftharpoons}} R_3Si^*XY$$

$$R_3Si^*XY \xrightarrow{k_2} R_3Si^*Y + X$$

On the steady-state approximation, simple kinetic analysis for mechanism S_N2^*-Si furnishes the following rate law:

$$\text{Rate} = \frac{d[R_3SiY]}{dt} = \frac{k_1}{k_{-1}} k_2[R_3SiX][Y]$$

which is equivalent to

$$\text{Rate} = \frac{d[R_3SiY]}{dt} = k_2 K_{eq.}[R_3SiX][Y]$$

Thus, the *observed* rate law for operation of mechanism S_N2^*-Si

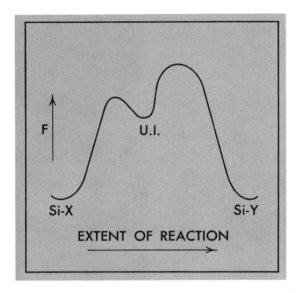

Fig. 11-5   Reaction profile for an S_N2^*-Si mechanism.

will appear to be that of a simple bimolecular displacement reaction, and kinetics is incapable of distinguishing between mechanisms S_N2-Si and S_N2^*-Si.   For both mechanisms, reaction rate will be a function of the first power of the concentrations of R_3SiX and Y.

However, detailed analysis shows that mechanism S_N2^*-Si must inevitably lead to products that are extensively or completely racemized.   The finding of many stereospecific reactions of R_3Si^*X argues strongly against extensive operation of this mechanism for reactions of R_3SiX.   Figure 11-5 is a reaction profile for mechanism S_N2^*-Si.

11-7   The S_N2^{**}-Si mechanism

This mechanism is defined as involving formation of a full-fledged pentacovalent-silicon intermediate, *five full bonds to central Si,* in a slow and rate-controlling step, followed by fast conversion of the intermediate to products in a second step.   The attacking reagent Y is a nucleophile.

In the following kinetic formulation for mechanism S_N2^{**}-Si,

$k_2 \gg k_{-1}$, $k_{-1} \gg k_1$, and the intermediate is unstable and obeys the steady-state approximation:

$$R_3Si^*X + Y \underset{k_{-1}}{\overset{k_1}{\rightleftharpoons}} R_3Si^*XY$$

$$R_3Si^*XY \overset{k_2}{\longrightarrow} R_3Si^*Y + X$$

On the steady-state approximation, simple kinetic analysis for mechanism S_N2^{**}-Si furnishes the following rate law:

$$\text{Rate} = \frac{d[R_3SiY]}{dt} = k_1[R_3SiX][Y]$$

Thus, the *observed* rate law for operation of mechanism S_N2^{**}-Si will appear to be that of a simple bimolecular displacement reaction, and kinetics is incapable of distinguishing between mechanisms S_N2-Si and S_N2^{**}-Si. For both mechanisms, reaction rate will be a function of the first power of the concentrations of R_3SiX and Y.

However, operation of mechanism S_N2^{**}-Si would involve formation of a pentacovalent-silicon intermediate without significant stretching of the Si—X bond, and the rate-controlling transition state for a reaction proceeding by this mechanism would be

$$Y---\overset{\textstyle R_3}{Si}----X \tag{11-1}$$

Transition state (11-1) is generally inconsistent with the large body of structure-reactivity data (see Chap. 8) which shows that increased capacity of —X to stabilize a negative charge generally enhances reaction rate for R_3SiX, independent of whether —X, in a given reaction series or in different reaction series, has closely similar polar effects (or electronegativities).

Furthermore, transition state (11-1) is completely inconsistent with the stereochemical facts for reactions of silicon-oxygen compounds. The dramatic change from inversion of configuration for R_3Si^*OCOR' to retention of configuration for R_3Si^*OR' with the same reagent is only explicable on the ground that the increased capacity of $R'COO—$ to stabilize a negative charge changes the mechanism from S_Ni-Si for R_3Si^*OR' to

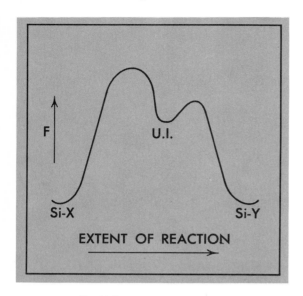

Fig. 11-6   Reaction profile for an S_N2^{**}-Si mechanism.

S_N2-Si for R_3Si^*OCOR'. The polar effects (and electronegativities) of —OR' and —$OCOR'$ must be closely similar, but their capacity for stabilizing a negative charge is vastly different.

On balance, the evidence from stereochemistry and reaction kinetics is fairly convincing on the point that mechanism S_N2^{**}-Si is uncommon for reactions of R_3SiX. However, there is one reaction series, (8-1), which may follow such a mechanism. That series involves base-catalyzed solvolysis of R_3SiH in ethanol-water media and has $\rho^* = +4.3$. However, nothing is known concerning the stereochemistry of such reactions, and stereochemical studies of other R_3Si^*H reactions carried out under different conditions indicate that these do not take place by mechanism S_N2^{**}-Si. Figure 11-6 is a reaction profile for mechanism S_N2^{**}-Si.

11-8 The principle of "least motion" of nonreacting groups

Many R_3Si^*X and R_4Si^* compounds can be distilled at temperatures in excess of 200° without loss of optical activity. This shows, at once, that the energy barrier to large distortion of the tetrahedral angles is considerable.   For thermal racemization of R_3Si^*X (without decomposition), an R—Si—R angle would have to expand (70.5°) to 180°, as would the R—Si—X angle.

Large expansion of angles is, of course, not impossible.   But the present author believes that the principle of "least motion" applies to the nonreacting groups in R_3Si^*X reactions.   If this limiting principle did not apply, it is difficult to see how so many reactions of R_3Si^*X could be stereospecific.

The postulate made here is that none of the stereospecific reactions of asymmetric silicon involve (70.5°) expansion of an R—Si—R angle to 180°; that the usual expansion of R—Si—R angles in inversion reactions is of the order of 10° to give R—Si—R angles of 120°; and that the usual contraction of R—Si—R angles in retention reactions is also of the order of 10° to give R—Si—R angles of 100°.

Application of the principle of "least motion" of nonreacting R groups, and the consequent assumption of nonlinear R—Si—R angles, is especially pertinent for S_Ni-Si reactions proceeding with pure retention of configuration.   For an S_Ni-Si mechanism involving a quasi six-ring transition state (e.g., Grignard reduction of R_3Si^*OMe), a linear arrangement for one R—Si—R angle, and an overall trigonal bipyramid arrangement with respect to Si, the following transition state would be possible:

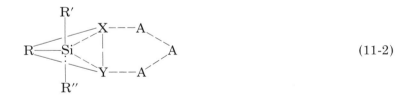

$$(11\text{-}2)$$

But detailed analysis (see below) shows that formation of transition state (11-2) followed by expulsion of X would result in formation of R_3Si^*Y with *inversion* of configuration.   *This is not observed.*

For the hypothetical case of X and Y equatorial in a trigonal bipyramid transition state, inversion of configuration should result from attack of Y at a back edge of the silicon tetrahedron as in I, followed by formation of transition state II, and conversion of II to the *inverted* product III.

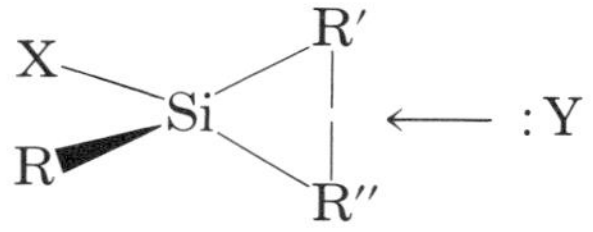

I

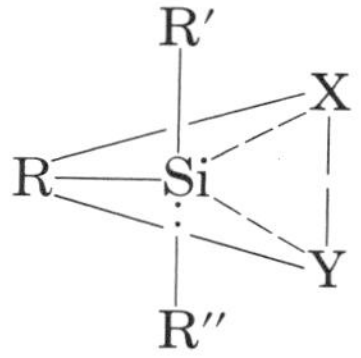

II

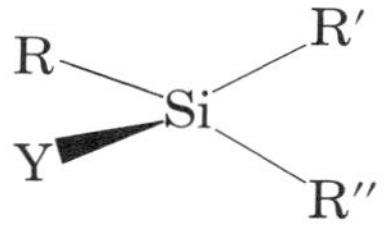

III

Thus, the actual mechanism of S_Ni-Si retention reactions proceeding via a quasi six-ring transition state involves a pyramidal arrangement of the three R groups with respect to the silicon atom—in accord with the principle of "least motion" for the nonreacting R groups.

11-9   The S_N2-Si stereochemistry rule and participation of the $3d_{z^2}$ orbital

The general stereochemistry rule of inversion of configuration for good leaving groups having pK_a of their conjugate acids less than ca. 6, regardless of the nature of the solvent, and providing only that Y is more basic than X, is a striking fact of organosilicon stereochemistry.[1] It is consistent with the orbital representation shown in Fig. 11-7 for an S_N2-Si transition state (Fig. 11-1) or unstable intermediate (Fig. 11-2).

In Fig. 11-7, X and Y use appropriate filled orbitals for overlap with two hybrid $3p_z3d_{z^2}$ orbitals of the central silicon. The R groups use sp^3 hybrid orbitals for overlap with $3s3p^2$ hybrid orbitals of the central silicon. Stereospecific inversion of

---

[1] Despite the fact that the pK_a of HF places —F in the category of good leaving groups, the high bond energy of Si—F (ca. 130 kcal./mole) and the relatively high capacity of —F for coordination with the electrophilic center of an attacking reagent frequently cause R_3Si^*F to react with retention of configuration by mechanism S_Ni-Si. The above rule is for acyclic cases.

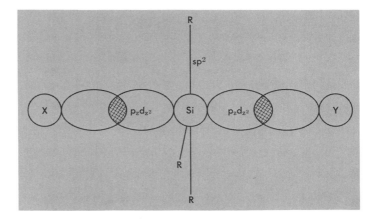

Fig. 11-7   Transition state for an S_N2-Si mechanism involving $3d_{z^2}$ orbital participation.

configuration for S_N2-Si reactions results from the straight-angle relationship of the two $3p_z3d_{z^2}$ hybrid orbitals.

The assumption of $3d_{z^2}$ orbital participation in S_N2-Si transition states is an attractive hypothesis. But it should be noted that the geometry of the $3p_z$ orbital, and overlap of appropriate orbitals of X and Y with the two lobes of the $3p_z$ orbital (analogous to S_N2 transition states for carbon), would also give inversion of configuration, even if $3d_{z^2}$ participation were insignificant. In short, the extent of $3d_{z^2}$ participation in S_N2-Si reactions can vary without changing the stereochemical outcome of such reactions. In some cases such participation may be quite small. This situation is shown in Fig. 11-8.

Fig. 11-8   Transition state for an S_N2-Si mechanism involving no $3d$ orbital participation.

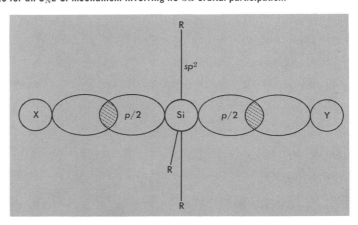

Regardless of the extent of $3d_{z^2}$ participation in S_N2-Si reactions, considering only the orbitals used by the central silicon, the Si—X bond will have less s character and more p character in the transition state, and the Si—R bonds will have more s character and less p character in the transition state. Thus, in S_N2-Si transition states or intermediates the Si - - - X and Y - - - Si "bonds" are relatively long and weak compared to the R—Si bonds.

This book on the stereochemistry of silicon and recent work with germanium and phosphorus compounds all indicate the general significance and applicability of the important discovery made by P. Walden in 1895.

Index of reactions

The detailed Contents serves the purpose of a general subject index, except for the omission of specific reactions. The concise Index of Reactions given below repairs this lack, and should be of use to the reader who wishes to look up the stereochemistry or kinetics of a specific type of reaction.

Each entry contains a formula having silicon followed by the reactive group. An asterisk associated with the silicon in the formula (e.g., Si*H) means that the entry refers to stereochemistry of reaction. The absence of an asterisk means that the entry refers to kinetics and/or structure-reactivity relationships.

Acyloxysilanes, Si*Cl and Hg(OAc)$_2$
  (*see* Mercuric acetate)
  Si*Cl and KOAc (*see* Potassium
    acetate)
  Si*OCOR, formation from Si*Cl and
    cyclo-C$_6$H$_{11}$NH$_3$OCOR, 81, 82
  Si*OK and RCOCl (*see* Silanolate)

Alcoholysis of, Si*Br, 83, 94, 163, 164
  Si*Cl, 79, 80, 93, 163, 164
  SiCl, 76, 77
  Si*OCOR, 69, 70, 73, 163, 164
  SiOMen*, 130–133
    acid- and base-catalyzed
      methanolysis, 131–133

Alkoxides, Si*OR, formation of (*see* Alcoholysis)

Boron trifluoride etherate, reaction with Si*OMen, 42
Bridgehead silicon reactions, base-catalyzed solvolysis of SiH, 156–158
  chloride-radiochloride exchange, 158, 159
  chlorination of SiH, 158
  hydrolysis and reduction of SiCl, 154–156
Bromination, of Si*H, 107–109, 111, 163, 164
  of SiH, 107, 108
Bromine, reaction with Si*—α-Np, 162–165
Bromine chloride, reaction with, Si*H, 108, 109
  SiH, 108, 109

Carbon-silicon cleavage, in β-chloroethylsilanes and β-hydroxyethylsilanes (*see* β-eliminations)
  of α-Np—Si* (*see* Bromine)
Carboxylates, Si*OCOR, formation of (*see* Acyloxysilanes)
Chlorination, of Si*H, 42, 107–109, 111, 163–165
  of SiH, 107–109, 127–130
Condensation of SiOH, 135–137
Coupling reactions (*see* Grignard reagent; Organolithium compounds)

Deuterium-hydrogen exchange, for Si*D plus LiAlH₄, 102–104
  for Si*H plus LiAlD₄, 102–104

β-Elimination, acid-catalyzed rates of SiCH₂CH₂OH, 144, 145
  neutral rates of SiCH₂CH₂Cl, 143, 144

Grignard reagent, reaction with Si*OMe, 59, 60

Halide-halide exchange, of Si*Br with *cyclo*-C₆H₁₁NH₃Cl, 96
  of Si*Br with *cyclo*-C₆H₁₁NH₃F, 163, 164
  of Si*Cl with *cyclo*-C₆H₁₁NH₃Cl[36], 98–100
  of Si*Cl with *cyclo*-C₆H₁₁NH₃F, 96, 163, 164
Hydrolysis of, Si*Br, 83, 93, 163, 164
  Si*Cl, 78, 93, 163, 164
  SiCl, 76, 77, 91, 92
  SiF, 138–143
    acid-catalyzed rates, 139, 141, 142
    equilibria, 139, 140
    neutral rates, 138, 139
  Si*OK, 49

Lithium aluminum hydride (*see under* Reduction)

Mercuric acetate, reaction with Si*Cl, 81, 93, 163, 164
Methanolysis (*see* Alcoholysis)
Methoxy-methoxy exchange, tritiated Si*OMe plus MeOH, 58
Methoxylation, of Si*Br with NaBH(OMe)₃, 83, 94
  of Si*Cl with methanol (*see* Alcoholysis)
  of Si*Cl with NaBH(OMe)₃, 81, 93
  of Si*Cl with NaB(OMe)₄, 80, 93, 163, 164

Organolithium compounds, reactions, with Si*Cl, 91, 92, 166–169
  with Si*F, 92, 166–171
  with Si*H, 169, 170
Organometallic reagents, reactions with Si*X (*see* Grignard reagent; Organolithium compounds)

Perbenzoic acid, reaction with Si*H, 110
Potassium acetate, reaction with Si*Cl, 81, 93, 164
Potassium hydroxide, powdered KOH(*s*), reactions, with Si*Br, 83, 94

Potassium hydroxide, with Si*Cl, 79, 93
 with Si*H, 104, 111, 163
 with Si*OCOR, 68, 69, 73, 163
 with Si*OR, 53, 54, 73, 163
 with Si*OSi*, 54–56, 73
 with SiOSi, 134, 135

Racemization, of Si*Cl by polar,
 aprotic solvents, 84–87
 of Si*Cl by salts, 97–100
 of Si*F by methanol without —F
  displacement, 88–91
Rearrangement of an optically active
 α-hydroxysilane, 56, 57
Reduction, Grignard, with t-BuMgCl,
 of Si*OMe, 50, 51, 73
 of Si*O-$cyclo$-C$_6$H$_{11}$, 50, 51, 73
 of Si*O-t-C$_4$H$_9$, 50, 51, 73
Reduction with LiAlH$_4$, of Si*Br, 83,
 94, 163–165
 of Si*Cl, 42, 83, 94, 163–165
 of Si*F, 87, 94, 164
 of Si*OCOR, 66–68, 73, 163, 164
 of Si*OH, 53, 73, 163, 164
 of Si*OR, 41, 51–53, 73, 163, 164
 of Si*OSi*, 53, 73
Reduction with NaBH$_4$ of Si*Cl, 83, 94

Resolution of
 ($\pm$)-α-NpPhMeSiO-(—)Men, 40,
 41

Silanolate, Si*OK, optical stability in
 xylene, 49
 reaction, with Me$_2$SO$_4$, 49
 with RCOCl, 49
 with Si*Br, 83, 94
 with Si*Cl, 82, 93
 with Si*F, 88, 94
 with Si*OTs, 70–73
Solvolysis, base-catalyzed, of
 Me$_3$SiCH$_2$C$_6$H$_4$X giving benzyl-
 silicon cleavage, 149
 of Si*H, in cyclohexanol, 106
 in t-butyl alcohol, 105, 106
Solvolysis in ethanol-water, acid-
 catalyzed, of Et$_3$SiOC$_6$H$_4$X,
 146–148
 of SiH, 128–130
 of SiOC$_6$H$_5$, 137, 138
 base-catalyzed, of Et$_3$SiOC$_6$H$_4$X,
 146–148
 of SiH, 127–130
 of SiOC$_6$H$_5$, 137, 138

Tosylate, Si*OTs, reaction with Si*OK,
 70–72